Ruskin the Painter
and his works at
Bembridge

Oxford University Press

Amen House, E.C. 4

London Edinburgh Glasgow New York
Toronto Melbourne Capetown Bombay
Calcutta Madras

Humphrey Milford

Publisher to the University

John Ruskin

from a drawing by George Richmond in the National Portrait Gallery

Ruskin the Painter
and his works at
Bembridge

by

J. Howard Whitehouse

President of the Ruskin Society, Master of Brantwood,
Warden of Bembridge School

Oxford University Press
London : Humphrey Milford

FIRST PUBLISHED 1938

PRINTED IN GREAT BRITAIN

To
my friend
William A. Cadbury

Contents

List of Illustrations

All except the frontispiece are from drawings by Ruskin

John Ruskin, from a drawing by George Richmond   *Frontispiece*

Ruskin the Painter

Ruskin the Painter

RUSKIN's eminence as a writer and social reformer has perhaps obscured the extraordinary service he rendered by his incomparable range of drawings. It would be true to say that if he had written no books and had assumed no leadership of men in a great transitional period of our history his name would have been honoured in history for the creative faculty which enabled him both to see and to interpret the spirit of beauty alike in nature and in the works of men.

I desire in this attempt to give some account of Ruskin's work as a painter, to consider first the influences which guided him to his life's work in which his powers of pencil and brush were to form a vital part. I must therefore recapitulate certain main features of his life as a boy and youth.

Boyhood

It is well known that Ruskin's boyhood from very early years was spent under conditions perhaps unique for a boy in the early nineteenth century. His father was a wealthy wine merchant and preserved the old habit of visiting his customers personally. Once or twice a year, with his wife and young son, he went by carriage through many of the most interesting parts of England, Wales, and Scotland.

These tours were a source of extraordinary value as well as interest to the boy. His father was a man of cultured taste and knowledge and made a practice of visiting all places of interest within reach, such as old houses, castles, and places famous for their beauty or literary associations, or for collections of pictures. In this way Ruskin acquired a knowledge of art and standards of judgement remarkable in so young a boy. Above all he developed his love of nature which had always been with him and was to become the most vital interest in his life and work.

His First Foreign Tour

On Ruskin's fourteenth birthday he was given a copy of Rogers's *Italy*. This book of poems was illustrated by vignettes by Turner which fascinated the boy. He was also much influenced by Prout's *Sketches in Flanders and Germany*. These books led to an extension of the family travels to foreign countries. This first foreign journey which Ruskin made with his parents at the age of fourteen took him by way of Calais and Brussels to Cologne, up the Rhine to Strasbourg, through the Black Forest to Schaffhausen, and then through north Switzerland and over Splügen to Como, Milan, and Genoa. In his autobiography Ruskin tells in moving language the influence which his first sight of the Alps had upon his whole life. This was the first of many journeys, for he travelled regularly abroad for most of his life, and in many years spent as much time on the Continent as in England.

From very early years Ruskin kept diaries with

great fidelity. As a boy he recorded his experiences and described the places he visited. He continued this in his foreign journeys and has left diaries covering a great part of his life.

His Early Drawings

As a very young boy he began the practice of drawing, and his earliest note-books are full of great interest, not only for the skill shown by so young a boy, but because they show certain great qualities which came to perfection in his later work.

Throughout the whole of his life Ruskin was to continue the plan he first adopted as a boy and illustrate his writings with his pencil or brush. A great amount of Ruskin's prose work would be incomplete, and its meaning partly lost, had he not been able to illustrate his theme with drawings.

His drawings fall into many categories. In boyhood and youth they are of interest and importance in tracing the development of his interests. They reflect, too, the ever-extending growth of his intellectual and spiritual life. The Bembridge collection shows a remarkable gift of draughtsmanship. The qualities of accuracy and sympathy are seen in everything he did. Above all, he had an extraordinary power of rendering details faithfully.

He was always interested in maps and those which he did as a boy of 8 or 9 show, in a very marked degree, his power in this connexion.

One of the earliest subjects to which he devoted

himself was architecture, and the drawings he did when no older than 16 are of remarkable beauty, for there was always something more in them than accurate draughtsmanship. His intense sympathy with his subject gave to all of them an imaginative atmosphere which lifted them far above mere records. The student may be referred in this connexion to the plates in this book showing drawings he made when about 16 years old at Fribourg, Munich, and Stuttgart. They are selected out of hundreds of others.

The youthful drawings of Ruskin reflect his passionate love of nature. Perhaps this is best seen in the numerous little studies he did when under the influence of the Turner vignettes in Rogers's *Italy*. Such drawings as those of Alpine scenes reproduced in this book might appear with Turner's without any obvious incongruity.

Ruskin's Masters

Ruskin, as an artist and draughtsman, was for the most part educated by himself. He had a great power of self-expression, an intense sympathy with nature, an aesthetic judgement which for the most part was accurate and far more sound than that of the popular verdicts of the day.

The signs of these dawning powers were with him as a boy:

> While yet a child, and long before his time,
> Had he perceived the presence and the power
> of greatness.

He was intensely industrious, he had noble guidance, he cared for literature and pictures, he sought on all occasions to express himself in verse and prose and, above all, to sketch the things he saw and loved. It was not until 1831, when he was 12, that he first had any formal instruction in drawing. His first master was Runciman who taught him the principles of perspective and was his drawing-master for many years. In 1836, when he was 17, he had lessons from Copley Fielding, the President of the old Water-Colour Society.

But Ruskin's real tutor was himself. He learnt quickly what others could teach him, but his amazing progress was due to his great industry and untiring delight in seeking to express himself in drawing. He was also greatly encouraged and helped by the study of the work of men he admired. Reference has already been made to Turner whose influence upon Ruskin at every stage of his life cannot be exaggerated. But there were others. He was much influenced by Prout and copied his style in his earlier drawings, as he often did in the case of Turner, and when he did not consciously copy the style of others in his own drawings he absorbed their teaching and spirit.

Two Aspects of his Work as Painter and Critic

It will help us to understand Ruskin's work both as a painter and as a philosopher if we remember that there were two main aspects of his practical work which we see reflected again and again in his teaching. He sought from time to time to express in his own drawings the beauty and the mystery of nature. He had seen in the work of Turner the revelation of a great seer who, while remaining true to the facts of nature, had done something more. He had seen a beauty unobserved and unknown by others. He had taken us beyond this beauty and opened our eyes to eternal truths. Ruskin began by giving us records of beauty which he had himself seen: his power to make these records marked all his working life, but they became something more than records, they became a great interpretation.

The Relation of his Art to his Books

This great quality is, of course, seen best in his illustrations to his own books. From the time he first began to write he illustrated many of these.

It is not generally recognized that a book like *Modern Painters* could not have been written in its present form had it not been possible for him to illustrate the book in part with his own drawings. These are a vital part of the book. No photographs, even if obtainable, could have served the same purpose. This can be realized by examining his drawing entitled 'Foreground Study', on p. 338 of the first volume of *Modern Painters* (Library edition), or the 'Study of Foliage' on p. 588 of the same volume. In *Modern Painters* Ruskin was in part examining the laws of beauty and was making a new contribution to a subject which in successive ages has occupied the greatest minds. As Professor Elton points out, he held that beautiful natural forms, in their perfection, are made for us to love, admire, and live by; so that the main or ultimate function of art, in representing them, comes at once into sight.

In elaborating this point of view Ruskin's power to illustrate his argument by his wonderful drawings from nature was an essential part of his work. How wonderful these drawings are! D. S. MacColl in his *Recreations and Reflections* thus describes them: 'He is a man subject to a rapt vision of delicate things such as the fibres of moss, the sculpturing and veining of rocks, the tracery of leaves, the lacework of foam, the changing fires of gems and clouds, vision compact of minute, tender, treasuring observation and of religious awe.'

The International Service of Ruskin's Art

It would be difficult to exaggerate the service which Ruskin has rendered to the cause of international understanding through the influence not only of his pen but of his pencil and brush. Let me take the case of Italy. No one has done for that country what Ruskin has done. He has written either in part or fully the history of many of her cities. What comparable work, for instance, has ever been done for Venice? In Ruskin's pages the history of this city is given in all its pageantry, success, and greatness. It is told as a chapter in human history and the story has all the elements of moving drama. But it is not only a history; it is a great interpretation of the art and genius of a people, giving life to stones, recreating a magical past. But the prose of Ruskin is only one of the instruments he uses to awaken our interest and sympathy. The painting, architecture, sculpture, and craftsmanship of Venice are made real to the reader because, entering with exquisite sympathy and understanding into the minds and meaning of the authors of these things, he is able to interpret them by his own drawings. His lovely drawings of details of buildings— the sculptured column, the carved tomb, the gothic window—gave the spirit of the original craftsman in the only adequate way. He succeeded in opening the eyes of countless people to an understanding, sometimes full, sometimes partial, but always inspiring, of the beauty and the meaning of certain forms of the expression of human genius.

What Ruskin did for Venice he did for many other cities in Italy and other countries. He does not only describe the art treasures of Rome, or Florence, or Assisi. These are related to their history, the character of their citizens, the achievements of an age. But everywhere he falls back upon his drawings for the real interpretation of the things he sees.

He brought knowledge of the treasures of Italy to countless people for the first time, and he created a new interest in the laws of beauty. He became an inspiring influence in the lives of great numbers of people who had never met him. The knowledge and influence and interest which he thus brought to so many was international. I mean that it helped to destroy insularity on the part of many who had never left this country.

He sent many abroad for the first time to visit the treasures and places he had drawn and described in his books. I have mentioned Italy in particular as the country for which he did so much, but of course he did similar service for France, Germany, Switzerland, as well as for his own country.

The Peacemaker

He thus became a great peacemaker, for the influence of his works and the spirit they generated became a liberalizing influence. Many of his disciples in this country found a great widening of their sympathies as a result of his art and teaching. They understood for perhaps the first time the genius of other nations, the part they had played in a great cultural civilization before their own country had emerged from comparative barbarism so far as art and beauty were concerned. They saw with new eyes the meaning of the spiritual unity of mankind, and they felt in consequence a friendship leading often to affection for the European nations. Thus we see people coming together under one of the best possible influences—that of a common admiration for things lovely and of good report.

This was no slight service to have accomplished in a not unimportant part of the life of Europe, and it is an influence which continues to this day.

Some General Characteristics

Although his drawings are of entrancing, delicate beauty Ruskin rarely sat down to paint a picture in the conventional sense. He always drew with a purpose. His brush was frequently his pulpit. He was always trying to open the eyes of those who would see the beauties of nature, and at all stages of his life some of his most lovely work consisted of details which many painters would have neglected. He was always ready and eager to record something he had seen of interest or beauty. But his immediate interest was to record, not to make a picture. An illustration of what I mean is seen in the drawing of alpine roses (plate 3 in this book). At first this looks like an attempt to give us a picture of mountains. He was only trying to show us the beauty of a cluster of alpine roses with an example of the environment in which they grew. So he drew thousands of similar details—the roofs covering a cluster of cottages, the summit of a tower, a sprig of growing ivy, a fragment of the rose dress of Botticelli's 'Spring', leaves in every sort of natural formation, a sculptured stone, a flying buttress, a flower in wrought iron, a peacock's feather, a tiny waterfall, a flower. He was always making records of little things of beauty. These drawings are unsurpassed for their delicacy and realism and have enabled many to appreciate the beauty of common things around them.

Ruskin's View on the Teaching of Drawing

In many branches of his work Ruskin was not merely a writer but one who had made practical experiments in connexion with the things he wrote about.

In social reform, for example, he had founded the Guild of St. George for practical experiment in the art of living together, he had repaired roads and had kept a retail shop in the interests of the poor, and had done hundreds of other things to carry out his own social teaching.

In his work as an artist he found himself at a comparatively early stage of his work compelled to write his views on how to draw, if only to deal with the great mass of correspondence which reached him as an acknowledged authority on all matters relating to art. But the process followed with other branches of his work was reversed. His practical experiments in social reform followed his writings on the subject. In the case of art his writings intended for the practical help of those wishing to draw followed his practical work as an artist and his work as a teacher at the Working Men's College.

The *Elements of Drawing* was published in 1857 and bore the title *The Elements of Drawing in Three Letters to Beginners.*

From the first Ruskin repudiated any intention to

make artists or professional designers. His book has
wider scope. He wanted to show the value of drawing
as a great cultural instrument in general education.
When giving evidence before a Royal Commission
in 1857 Ruskin said: 'My efforts are directed not
to making a carpenter an artist, but to making him
happier as a carpenter.' E. T. Cook well expressed
Ruskin's object: 'What he claimed for his system
was that it was calculated to teach refinement of perception; to train the eye in close observation of
natural beauties and the hand in delicacy of mani-
pulation; and thus to make his pupils to understand
what masterly work meant, and to recognize it when
they saw it.'

If the fundamental purpose of the book is remembered it adds greatly to its value as an instrument
of education, and its importance will be more ade-
quately realized.

Amongst the practical suggestions which Ruskin
makes in the *Elements of Drawing* are the following:

1. To give full importance from the first to local
colour. Leonardo, he reminded his readers, thus
wrote in his *Treatise on Painting*:

'The student who is desirous of making great pro-
ficiency in the art of imitating the works of nature
should not only learn the shape of figures or other
objects and be able to delineate them with truth
and precision, but he must also accompany them
with their proper lights and shadows according to
the situation in which those objects appear.'

2. To copy faithfully and without alteration whatever object he chooses to study.

3. He advised his students that perspective was of no value except in rudimentary work. 'You can draw the rounding line of a table in perspective, but you cannot draw the sweep of a sea bay.'

It would be outside my scope to attempt to give in detail the many suggestions and directions which Ruskin gives in this book. He writes simply and sympathetically. The chapter on sketching from nature is one which would tend to inspire any youth, however ignorant he may be.

His directions are detailed and easily understood but he does something greater. He awakens the sympathy of his reader for the object of drawing— the understanding of nature, at least the beginning of appreciation of its mystery and beauty.

Not the least service which he does is to help the student to understand the methods of the great masters such as Turner and Dürer. The facsimile which he gives of an etching from Turner showing hills, trees, and figures, with his description of the principles of its composition, makes an unforgettable lesson. The student who copies this drawing as Ruskin advised has been set upon a road which will lead him to great discoveries, ever increasing in interest and value.

Ruskin goes into many details for the help of the students for whom he wrote the book. Thus he gives careful advice on the mixing of colours.

D

A specially interesting part of the book is entitled 'Things to be Studied'. Here he gives a list of the masters 'whom you may safely admire and a few of the books which you may safely possess'. The masters include Prout, Cruikshank, Bewick, Blake, Richter, Rossetti. The books include Bacon, Johnson, Scott's novels, Homer, Plato, Aeschylus, Herodotus, Dante, Shakespeare, and Spenser.

The *Elements of Perspective*, which followed the *Elements of Drawing* two years later, was intended to be complementary to the latter work. It is illustrated throughout by a great number of diagrams and propositions in the manner of Euclid.

Ruskin's Copies of Pictures

One branch of Ruskin's art, though not original, was pursued by him with so much skill and definite purpose as to make it an important contribution to his work as a painter. From early boyhood, for the whole of his working life, he devoted much time and concentrated labour upon making copies of great pictures or details from them. He insisted upon the importance of such work in all his teaching, and his students did much of it under his guidance. By making studies from the masters he saw the best way of enabling students to understand their methods and the way in which they surmounted difficulty. In this way, too, students gained experience in such matters as composition, perspective, and colour.

His own copies are a permanent enrichment of

our art. In the Bembridge collections there are many examples. There are superb studies after Tintoretto, Botticelli, Veronese, and many more. These in themselves are great pictures, and bring to those who see them and may never be able to see the originals a knowledge and appreciation, perhaps not otherwise obtainable, of some of the world's greatest art treasures.

But he did much more than merely make copies of great pictures. He described them with eloquence and vision, and thus did more to arouse general enthusiasm for art and its message than perhaps any other writer.

I take as an example of his sympathetic and attractive descriptions of pictures some of the comments he makes on Tintoretto's 'Adoration of the Magi', in the S. Rocco at Venice, of which Ruskin's large water-colour copy is in the Bembridge collection:

The most finished picture in the Scuola except the 'Crucifixion', and perhaps the most delightful of the whole. It unites every source of pleasure that a picture can possess; the highest elevation of principal subject, mixed with the lowest detail of picturesque incident; the dignity of the highest ranks of men, opposed to the simplicity of the lowest; the quietness and serenity of an incident in cottage life, contrasted with the turbulence of troops of horsemen and the spiritual power of angels. The placing of the two doves as principal points of light in the front of the picture, in order to remind the spectator of the poverty of the mother whose child is receiving the offerings and adoration of three monarchs, is one of Tintoret's master touches; the whole scene, indeed, is conceived in his happiest manner. Nothing can be at once more humble or more dignified than the bearing of the kings; and there is a sweet reality given to the whole incident by the Madonna's stooping forward and lifting her hand in admiration of the vase of gold which has been set before the Christ, though she does so with such gentleness and quietness that her dignity is not in the least injured by the simplicity of the action. As if to illustrate the means by which the Wise Men were brought from the East, the whole picture is nothing but a large star, of which the Christ is the centre; all the figures, even the timbers of the roof, radiate from the small bright figure on which the countenances of the flying angels are bent, the star itself, gleaming through the timbers above, being quite subordinate. The composition would almost be too artificial were it not broken by the luminous distance, where the troop of horsemen are waiting for the kings. These, with a dog running at full speed, at once interrupt the symmetry of the lines, and form a point of relief from the over-concentration of all the rest of the action.

In the later pages of this book the reader will find other examples of his descriptions of pictures and sculpture, as of Veronese's 'Cuccina Family' and the tomb of Ilaria at Verona. His account of these works is quoted on pp. 71–3 and 49–50, and reproductions of Ruskin's copies of them will be found in this volume.

I have found in my personal experience that Ruskin's copies of great pictures with his eloquent interpretations are powerful instruments for awakening interest and enthusiasm in the mind of youth.

I have found too that Ruskin's advice to make the copying of pictures by great painters a part of art training is of profound importance.

Ruskin's Views on the Place of Art in Education

Ruskin was a pioneer in urging many reforms in education. This was especially true in connexion with the place of drawing in education. The fundamental principle which controlled all his teaching was that everybody ought to be taught to draw just as everybody ought to be taught to read and write. His great disciple, William Morris, at a later date expressed his belief in this principle in the same words.

In a letter which he wrote in 1858, giving his advice which had been asked for in connexion with the establishment of certain Art examinations at the University of Oxford, he suggested that the first object of such an examination should be 'to put the happiness and knowledge which the study of art conveys within the conception of the youth, so that he may in after life pursue them if he has the gift'.

In the same letter he stated that 'the facts which

an elementary knowledge of drawing enables a man to observe and note are often of as much importance to him as those which he can describe in words or calculate in numbers'.

He saw in the practice of drawing a great spiritual influence. In *A Joy for Ever* he wrote:

> In our simplest codes of school instruction I hope some day to see local natural history assume a principal place, so that our peasant children may be taught the nature and uses of the herbs that grow in their meadows, and may take an interest in observing and cherishing, rather than in hunting and killing, the harmless animals of their country.

The Unity of Ruskin's Teaching

The criticism has often been made that Ruskin is contradictory in his writings on many subjects. Such criticism is shallow. Ruskin's published writings date from the time when he was a very young boy to the years of his old age, and it would be indeed remarkable if he believed at 70 all the things which he believed at 7. There is no fundamental contradiction in the general spirit of everything which he wrote. When we consider his writings on the more limited question of the value of drawing we find a like consistency. At the age of 19 he wrote on the advantages of drawing for young people and he set them forth as follows:

1. The power of appreciating fine pictures.

2. An agreeable and interesting occupation for many hours.

3. The habit of quick observation and the exquisite perception of the beauties of nature.

4. The power of amusing and gratifying others.

He never tired of pressing the vital good which came from the practice of drawing. In *The Laws of Fiesole* he states: 'The duty of art is to teach but to teach pleasantly. She is shamed, not exalted, when she has only graces to display.'

He was always desirous that every vital need in education should be provided for in all schools. Thus he pleaded for children to have access to good prints. He wished to see provided for them nursery tales, for these could often be obtained illustrated with good woodcuts. He particularly praises Richter as an inspiring master to study. He emphasizes the fact that all good schools enforce delicacy of drawing and subtlety of sight. All great art, he tells us, is delicate.

The Mission of Art

In *The Two Paths*, Ruskin has expressed some aspects of the mission of art which remain quite unshakable amidst the discordance of contending schools.

Art enabled them to say and to see what they could not otherwise say or see, and it also enabled them to learn certain lessons which they could not otherwise learn.

First, it enabled them to say things which they

could not otherwise say. There were thousands of
things in this world which they could not say,
unless they drew them. They might write long
journals, they might write long descriptions; but
if they could not draw, they could not exhibit to
others the forms of things, the aspects of places,
or the effects of machines. If organic existence
were required to be described—if they wanted to
depict the most important facts connected with
any country—they must be able to draw; and
hundreds of other points of information might be
required to be described, and yet such a description could not be given unless they had the power
of expressing themselves by their pencils. In a
hundred ways they could communicate information to other people by the pencil, which they
could not do by any other means. And that was
the way reading first became popular. The man
to whom England owed so much to this day—
whose skill and knowledge were so great, who
was almost her best scholar—was induced to read
his first book by the promise of his mother that
she would give him one having beautiful pictures
in it; and because of the beautiful pictures on the
margin of the book King Alfred learned to read.
In that way drawing was to this hour of enormous
influence with the art of printing and of reading.
And that especially because it was not so mis-
leading. It was very difficult to get good literature, and bad reading hurt students in two ways—

it told them false things, and it wasted their time and faculties; and he was not altogether sure it was a greater certain advantage for people of a certain class of mind to know how to read than the contrary. He was not quite sure whether there were not agitations of mind, tumults of heart, waste of time, acquaintance with things which people should not know, excitement of feelings, and many other evils which might be set against the good of good and serviceable books, which were not always of the popular taste. The greatest good was to be derived from the reading of one book. Some classes of books ought to be burned altogether. The power of expressing and power of obtaining knowledge ought to be taught to every child, according to his powers of acquirement.

It is no mean achievement to fire the enthusiasm of youth as they begin the study and practice of art with words such as these.

Drawing a Vital Education

It is interesting to see that Ruskin's message on the value of drawing was as certain and clear in the later years of his life as it was at the beginning. The passage which follows is of particular interest to every one interested in Ruskin's teaching, for he not only gives in these words the ideal of true education, but he has something to say about Oxford which to-day seems, as it is, the view of a prophet.

I have said enough, I think, to induce you to

bear with me in the statement of my main theorem —that reading and writing are in no sense education, unless they contribute to this end of making us feel kindly towards all creatures; but that drawing, and especially physiologic drawing, is vital education of a most precious kind. Farther, that more good would be done by any English nobleman who would keep his estate lovely in its native wildness; and let every animal live upon it in peace that chose to come there, than will be done, as matters are going now, by the talk of all the Lords in Parliament as long as we live to listen to them; and I will even venture to tell you my hope, though I shall be dead long before its possible fulfilment, that one day the English people will, indeed, so far recognize what education means as to surround this university with the loveliest park in England, twenty miles square; that they will forbid, in that environment, every unclean, mechanical, and vulgar trade and manufacture, as any man would forbid them in his own garden;—that they will abolish every base and ugly building, and nest of vice and misery, as they would cast out a devil;—that the streams of the Isis and Cherwell will be kept pure and quiet among their fields and trees; and that, within this park, every English wild flower that can bloom in lowland will be suffered to grow in luxuriance, and every living creature that haunts wood and stream know that it has happy refuge.

These words were addressed to the under-graduates of Oxford in 1872, just sixty-six years ago. The formal response in Oxford came a few years ago with the formation of the Oxford Preservation Trust. Ruskin had told them what would be necessary more than half a century earlier.

Art not an Unrelated Subject in Education

Ruskin has dealt with every phase of education in connexion with the responsibility of schools to provide adequate facilities for the knowledge and practice of art. But it is never an unrelated subject. This is again shown in *Fors*.

Every parish school to have garden, playground, and cultivable land round it, or belonging to it, spacious enough to employ the scholars in fine weather mostly out of doors.

Attached to the building, a children's library, in which the scholars who *care* to read may learn that art as deftly as they like, by themselves, helping each other without troubling the master; —a sufficient laboratory always, in which shall be specimens of all common elements of natural substances, and where simple chemical, optical, and pneumatic experiments may be shown; and according to the size and importance of the school, attached workshops, many or few,—but always a carpenter's, and first of those added in the better schools, a potter's.

In the school itself, the things taught will be

music, geometry, astronomy, botany, zoology, to all; drawing, and history, to children who have gift for either. And finally, to all children of whatever gift, grade, or age, the laws of Honour, the habit of Truth, the Virtue of Humility, and the Happiness of Love.

Many years before these words were written, he had thus expressed himself:

I believe there is no child so dull or so indolent but it may be roused to wholesome exertion by putting some practical and personal work on natural history within its range of daily occupation; and, once aroused, few pleasures are so innocent, and none so constant. I have often been unable, through sickness or anxiety, to follow my own art work, but I have never found natural history fail me, either as a delight or a medicine. But for children it must be curtly and wisely taught. We must *show* them things, not tell them names. A deal chest of drawers is worth many books to them, and a well-guided country walk worth a hundred lectures.

Natural History

Ruskin has related his advocacy of drawing to its vital use for the study of many other subjects. Thus, for instance, when he was Slade Professor at Oxford he showed the essential connexion of drawing with natural history, and said these words to the students in 1870:

While I myself hold this professorship, I shall direct you in these exercises very definitely to natural history, and to landscape; not only because in these two branches I am probably able to show you truths which might be despised by my successors; but because I think the vital and joyful study of natural history quite the principal element requiring introduction, not only into University, but into national education, from highest to lowest; and I even will risk incurring your ridicule by confessing one of my fondest dreams, that I may succeed in making some of you English youths like better to look at a bird than to shoot it; and even desire to make wild creatures tame, instead of tame creatures wild.

He showed, too, that in some ways drawing is essential to get certain knowledge in some branches of natural history. 'Take a spray of ling', he says in *Proserpina*, 'and you will find that the richest piece of Gothic spire sculpture would be dull and graceless beside the grouping of the floral masses in their various life. But it is difficult to give the accuracy of attention necessary to see their beauty without drawing them.'

In a letter to a correspondent, in 1853, he pleaded for a synthesis in many branches of education.

I think it would be much *more* sensible to consider drawing as in some degree teachable in concurrence with other branches of education. Geography, for instance, ought to introduce drawing maps and shapes of mountains. Botany, shapes of leaves. History, shapes of domestic utensils, &c. I think I could teach a boy to draw without setting *any* time *apart* for drawing, and I would make him at the same time learn everything else quicker by putting the graphic element into other studies.

The Influence of the Ruskin Collection at Bembridge

All the works described in this book are in the collection of Ruskin's works at Bembridge School. They are exhibited in two galleries, well lighted and designed, and in addition to the pictures they contain examples of most of the arts and crafts of the country.

The Ruskin collection has been used for the purpose of its general cultural value in education. I have thought, therefore, that it would be of interest if I described the methods in which the collection has been used, and some of the results which have followed. The picture collection in the two galleries mentioned is not confined to Ruskin's works. Other painters are represented by original work, especially those who are associated with Ruskin. They include Albert Goodwin, R.A., Walter Crane, Sir Edward Burne-Jones, Sir John Millais, Albert Rutherston, T. M. Rooke, Samuel Prout, W. G. Collingwood, Samuel Lawrence, C. Fairfax Murray, Edward Clifford, Arthur Severn, Joseph Severn, and others.

The works of these painters will be treated in a separate volume.

The galleries are open free to the general public on application. They are, of course, primarily intended for the use of the school and they are visited by the boys singly or in little groups, or by forms. Boys may obtain permission to visit the galleries at any reasonable time. On Sunday afternoons throughout a large part of the year receptions are held to which each form in the school is invited in turn. At these receptions there is no attempt to encourage boys to look at the whole collection. They are asked to interest themselves in one or two pictures only during one visit. The usual method adopted at these receptions is first to give an informal talk on two or three interesting pictures in the collection. Questions and discussion are invited on any points in which any boy is interested and frequently a very helpful exchange of views takes place. Afterwards the boys wander round the galleries examining whatever they wish to look at and freely asking questions.

We have found this a sound method for encouraging the interest of boys in pictures and for helping to give them standards of taste and judgement. Such visits to the galleries may be made of very vivid interest, even if only one picture is talked about to the group. There are, for instance, many drawings of famous buildings in many parts of Europe. There is thus the opportunity to discuss historical, architectural, and social questions. The copies of great

masters give other opportunities. It is not difficult
to interest boys in the personality, life, and times of
men like Michelangelo and Tintoretto. Sometimes
an hour is devoted to nature-study drawings, animals or birds or flowers, and boys who are interested
in these subjects get many fresh ideas. Sometimes
the theme considered is that of sculpture, and it is
not difficult to interest the audience in the romance
behind many examples. Sometimes drawings of
foreign cities are specially examined and such a
subject never fails to excite general interest. These
informal receptions with a definite though not a dogmatic object, and which never lose their friendly informal atmosphere, must be counted as an important
means of using the collection for cultural purposes.

It is not an exaggeration to say that a boy who
becomes interested in a single great picture or in a
single great painter has received a permanent key by
which he can unlock further rooms in the mansion of
art. He learns too not to be frightened of pictures.
There is no attempt to give him any dogmatic views
about art. There is a definite desire to encourage
him to think for himself on certain lines of beauty
of universal significance, ageless in themselves.

The growing interest in art is helped by occasional
informal talks on great painters with lantern views
of some of their works. There is, in connexion with
the galleries, a large collection of lantern slides for
the help and interest of the boys.

A further agency for extending interest is a specialized art library. Many of the books in this library contain important illustrations. The books include many of the great biographies of painters and many works of criticism. This specialized library is distinct from the general school library, and is specially for the help of boys whose interest in art is already obvious or which is awakening.

Yet another method employed is to encourage boys to make copies of some of the pictures on the walls. Many of them are very suitable for this purpose and the method enables the student to realize the delicacy of line, the beauty of design, the superb draughtsmanship of the originals. The method gives an understanding of the painter's mind which is of great value. It is one of the methods which Ruskin himself always urged in connexion with art as an instrument of education.

Finally, it should not be assumed that the object of this great collection at Bembridge is to make professional painters. It has a far greater object. It is to make art an influence in the spiritual and intellectual life of the boy, to open his eyes to the beauty of the world around him, to enable him to understand the labours of great minds in the past and the heritage they have given him, to bring into his own life some understanding of the laws of beauty and to enable him to live a fuller and happier life.

Ruskin's Guidance To-day
There has recently been a great deal of criticism

with reference to the action of the Forestry Commissioners in planting large areas in the Lake District with young conifers, so that in a few years the character of the landscape where such planting takes place will be vitally changed. This work is controlled by the Forestry Commissioners, a body which, though appointed under Act of Parliament by the Government, is not under the control of Parliament. No Minister can be cross-examined or controlled in the House of Commons for his responsibility. I am in full sympathy with all the appeals which have been made to stop what I regard as vandalism, though I think it has often been done in ignorance of the damage which must follow. I want to put an aspect of the question which has been overlooked and which can be appreciated through the study of Ruskin's work and drawings.

Ruskin's old home, Brantwood, in which he spent the last thirty years of his life, looks across Coniston Water to one of the most magnificent views to be found in the country. It is one of the few places from which you can see a great mountain in its completeness, from its mighty roots on the shores of the lake to its summit. It is a great mountain of rock. Its ridges and buttresses and tarns, the lines of its splendid curves, not only give us an unforgettable picture of the majesty of nature but they tell a great story which the earnest scientist and the humble student can decipher. They tell us a story of the ages, and make clear something of the order and beauty and mystery and majesty of nature. Such a place is a great repository. Now no doubt its valleys and crevices and slopes of shallow soil can be used for the growing of great masses of these alien trees. But if this is done it means the destruction of those things and that knowledge which are amongst our most precious possessions. We should deliberately destroy something which is priceless and beyond the works of man. Ruskin has given us in advance the answer to the Forestry Commissioners. He has drawn the mountains as they were fashioned in the mighty mould of nature. He has shown us every beauty, but he has done much more than this. He has at least hinted at their secret and in part has revealed it. He has shown us that they supply the explanation, more exact, more scientific than we had ever dreamed of, of the laws of beauty. We have now in our own day and generation the opportunity to show the living influence of Ruskin by refusing any longer to support from a public body conduct which is indefensible.

We buy up old houses and properly preserve them, we protect a view or an ancient bridge, or the banks of a little rivulet—we properly do these things, but shall we at the same time look on whilst some of the greatest natural treasures, in what is the most wonderful repository of beauty which we have, are destroyed?

I have said that the body of Commissioners concerned is not responsible to Parliament, but Parliament which made can unmake; nor can I believe that the House of Commons will remain deaf to the appeals that are made to them in this connexion.

A careful study of Ruskin's works will enable the student to detect and to appreciate certain outstanding characteristics. When he looks at his architectural drawings he will be impressed by the superb draughtsmanship and by some quality difficult to analyse which conveys a sense of beauty. It is also an interpretation. We are, however, able not only to realize the beauty of the building but to understand something of the purpose of the builder. It is as though we heard the ancient craftsmen speak. These architectural drawings of Ruskin show his great sincerity and amazing accuracy. No detail is too trivial to escape him. It would be difficult indeed to visit any buildings which Ruskin had drawn without finding them invested with new beauty and interest. The drawings are related to the written word and so his prose and his art become a great unity.

When we leave his architectural sketches for his more general treatment of landscapes we see the same qualities, the interpretation of beauty and a power of noble composition. If sometimes he was inclined to depreciate the too careful study of perspective in the young artist, he himself was a master of it. Many of Ruskin's drawings of landscapes make delightful studies in the art of town and country planning and could often be usefully considered from that standpoint.

When we turn to his drawings of sculpture—the

great tombs of Verona, the glories of the greatest
of all gothic buildings in Venice—we are again in the
presence of an interpreter who gives us new visions
of beauty, and sends us far beyond the immediate
object drawn in the interest he creates within us.

When we turn to Ruskin's nature drawings, his
beautiful studies of living birds, his trees in every
stage of growth, isolated leaves, scraps of climbing
plants, these things in nature take on a new meaning for us, and we become prepared for the greater
lessons of his work when we turn to his cloud and
mountain studies and the higher grandeurs of nature
—storm-clouds on mountain ranges, the majesty of
the High Alps, the mighty cleavages of nature in
the gigantic rocks.

When we turn from all these subjects and look at
his copies of great pictures through the ages, of
Michelangelo, Titian, Tintoretto, Fra Angelico,
Botticelli, and the great painter, to the interpretation
of whose genius he devoted so much loving labour,
Turner, we realize that here is a man who wished to
make a record of all things of beauty and had the
necessary knowledge and judgement to do so. He
becomes through his works the guardian of the
things that are lovely and of good report.

Ruskin's works at
Bembridge School

Ruskin's works at Bembridge School

1. Tomb of Ilaria di Caretto, Cathedral of Lucca
Water-colour

This work was one which Ruskin regarded with great admiration, and there are numerous references to it in his books. The earliest description was given in a letter to his father, dated May 6, 1845: 'When the rose tints leave the clouds I go and stand a quarter of an hour beside the tomb of Ilaria di Caretto. It is in the cathedral. She was the second wife of Paolo Guinigi, signore of Lucca in 1430. He left the Lucchese several laws which they have still, but in a war with the Florentines he was betrayed by his allies and died in a prison in Pavia. The tower of his palace fortress is overgrown with copsewood, but the iron rings to which his horses used to be fastened still are seen along the length of the street before it; and the hooks by which the silken draperies were suspended on festal days.

'This, his second wife, died young and her monument is by Jacopo della Quercia, erected soon after her death. She is lying on a simple pillow with a hound at her feet. Her dress is of the simplest, middle-aged character, folding closely over the bosom and tight to the arms and clasped about the neck. Round her hair is a circular fillet with three star-shaped flowers. From under this the hair falls like that of the Magdalene, its undulation felt as it touches the cheek and no more. The arms are not folded, nor the hands clasped nor raised. Her arms are laid softly at length upon her body and her hands crossed as they fall. The drapery flows over the feet and half hides the hound. It is impossible to tell you the perfect sweetness of the lips and closed eyes, nor the solemnity of the seal of death which is set upon the whole figure. The sculpture—as art—is in every way perfect: truth itself but truth selected with inconceivable refinement of feeling. The cast of the drapery for severe natural simplicity and perfect grace I never saw equalled, nor the fall of the hands; you expect every instant, nay rather you seem to see every instant, the last sinking into death. There is no decoration nor work about it, not even enough for protection; you may stand beside it, leaning on the pillow and watching the twilight fade off the sweet dead lips and arched eyes in their sealed close.'

2. The tomb of Can Signorio della Scala, Verona
Pencil

Few drawings show better than this Ruskin's genius for drawing architectural subjects. It is a very remarkable piece of work and repays careful study. It is a monument of almost infinite detail, from the beautiful gothic arch at the base to the equestrian statue at the summit. If the middle portion of the drawing is examined it will be seen that in that part alone there are at least eight statues drawn more or less completely, in addition to a large number of beautiful details in stone. Look, for instance, at the exquisite stonework on the pyramid in the centre of the picture. This drawing stands out among the great number of noble studies which Ruskin made.

In vol. III of *The Stones of Venice*, Ruskin deals with the great gothic tombs at Venice, Verona, and elsewhere. In chapter ii, section 56, he thus refers to the tomb of Can Signorio della Scala: 'Close to this monument (that of Can Mastino della Scala) is another, the stateliest and most sumptuous of the three; it first arrests the eye of the stranger, and long detains it,—a many pinnacled pile, surrounded by niches with statues of the warrior saints.

'It is beautiful, for it still belongs to the noble time, the latter part of the fourteenth century; but its work is coarser than that of the other, and its pride may well prepare us to learn that it was built for himself, in his own lifetime, by the man whose statue crowns it, Can Signorio della Scala. Now observe, for this is infinitely significant. Can Mastino II was feeble and wicked, and began the ruin of his house; his sarcophagus is the first which bears upon it the image of Virtue, but he lays claim only to Fortitude. Can Signorio was twice a fratricide, the last time when he lay upon his death-bed: *his* tomb bears upon its gables the images of six Virtues,—Faith, Hope, Charity, Prudence, and (I believe) Justice and Fortitude.'

3. Astronomy and Music, Spanish Chapel, Florence

Water-colour

Ruskin, of course, devoted much study to the famous so-called Spanish Chapel at Santa Maria Novella in Florence. He has written of it at great length in *Mornings in Florence*, to which the reader is referred.

Amongst the treasures contained in this wonderful chapel are frescoes consisting of symbolical figures of the Arts and Sciences. At the feet of the figures are paintings of personages representative of the arts or sciences depicted.

This drawing shows, on the left, a figure symbolizing Astronomy, with Zoroaster underneath. On the right is Music, with Tubal-Cain as its representative.

As an example of Ruskin's vivid, intimate description of all places about which he wrote, the following brief extract from *Mornings in Florence* is given descriptive of these frescoes:

'She (Astronomy) wears a dark purple robe; holds in her left hand the hollow globe with golden zodiac and meridians: lifts her right hand in noble awe.

'"When I consider the heavens, the work of Thy

fingers, the moon and the stars, which Thou hast ordained."

'Crowned with gold, her dark hair in elliptic waves, bound with glittering chains of pearl. Her eyes dark, lifted.

'Beneath her, Zoroaster, entirely noble and beautiful, the delicate Persian head made softer still by the elaborately wreathed silken hair, twisted into the pointed beard, and into tapering plaits, falling on his shoulders. The head entirely thrown back, he looks up with no distortion of the delicately arched brow: writing, as he gazes.'

Concerning the figure of Music, on the right, Ruskin thus writes: 'This figure has been one of the loveliest in the series, an extreme refinement and tender severity being aimed at throughout. She is crowned, not with laurel, but with small leaves,—I am not sure what they are, being too much injured: the face thin, abstracted, wistful; the lips not far open in their low singing; the hair rippling softly on the shoulders. She plays on a small organ, richly ornamented with Gothic tracery, the slope of it set with crockets like those of Santa Maria del Fiore. Simon Memmi means that *all* music must be "sacred". Not that you are never to sing anything but hymns; but that whatever is rightly called music, or work of the Muses, is divine in help and healing.

'The actions of both hands are singularly sweet. The right is one of the loveliest things I ever saw done in painting. She is keeping down one note only, with her third finger, seen under the raised fourth; the thumb, just passing under; all the curves of the fingers exquisite, and the pale light and shade of the rosy flesh relieved against the ivory white and brown of the notes. Only the thumb and end of the forefinger are seen on the left hand, but they indicate enough its light pressure on the bellows. Fortunately, all these portions of the fresco are absolutely intact.'

4. Baden, Switzerland

Water-colour. 1862 or 1863

Inscribed 'Baden, Switzerland. First try of large subject. 36 R Catalogue J. Ruskin 1862 or 63'

There are some very interesting features in this unfinished drawing. The extraordinarily sympathetic drawing of the houses on the hill in the top right-hand corner of the picture should be noticed. The other details, where finished, are done with similar care. The mass effect of the towers and roofs is most striking.

5. Fribourg: The Watch Tower

Water-colour

A very delicate drawing showing the tower in great detail. There is a beautiful blue atmosphere suggested in the distance. The careful drawing of other buildings on the surrounding hills should also be noticed. How beautifully done is the foundation upon which the tower rests.

6. Mountain Rocks and Alpine Rose

Water-colour

Ruskin's intention here was not to draw a picture of mountain scenery, but to show us the conditions in which the Alpine Rose grows. The rose is delicately drawn on the left of the picture, and its environment is realistically given.

7. Bremgarten: Buildings and River

Pen, pencil, and wash. 1860

A typical drawing showing the artist's power of sympathetic treatment of architectural detail.

8. Near Brescia

Water-colour

A study of sky and trees. The latter are done with great delicacy.

9. Lake of Brienz from the Giessbach

Ink, pencil, and wash. 1866

A delicate piece of work showing branches of trees overhanging the water. Mountains are outlined in the distance.

10. Ducal Palace, Venice. Spandril decoration

Inscribed 'J. Ruskin Spandril Decoration The Ducal Palace'

This careful drawing is one of many which he made for *The Stones of Venice*. This was reproduced in vol. IX, page 352, plate XIV, of the Library edition.

11. Village near Lucerne

Water-colour

Inscribed 'J. R. Lucerne'

A walled-in village amongst the hills near Lucerne. The country around is vividly shown.

12. Lucerne and Alps

Pencil and water-colour. 1862

Inscribed 'Lucerne and Alps from hill above Reuss. J. Ruskin. Nov. 1862 $\frac{A}{2}$'

12a. Lucerne and Alps

Pencil and water-colour. 1862

Inscribed 'Lucerne and Alps from Reuss bank. J. Ruskin 1862. $\frac{B}{2}$'

The above are two slight drawings done above the town and showing Lucerne surrounded by hills. The town is seen outlined almost in the centre of the drawings.

13. Gothic Canopies

1. Fringe round a window, Rouen Cathedral
2. Eight-foiled aperture, Salisbury
3. Moulding from 5
4. Moulding from 6

5. Canopy from southern lateral porch, Abbeville
6. Canopy from the tomb of Can Grande at Verona
Ink, pencil, and wash

These exquisite architectural drawings are reproduced in *The Stones of Venice*, Library edition, vol. x, page 262, plate XII.

The drawing on the left (at foot) is of a particularly delicate nature.

14. Pistoja: Tower and Bridge connecting buildings

Ink and wash
Inscribed 'J. R. Pistoja'

A hasty and unfinished sketch but containing a surprising amount of detail. Notice particularly the little balcony at the right end of the bridge and the arches of the windows of the building on the right of the drawing.

15. Trees, Walls and Roofs

Water-colour

A little fragment, but delicately though hastily done. In the left foreground there is a wall with a tiny tower.

16. Study of Trees

Water-colour

A remarkable drawing both as regards details and mass effect. The grasses and flowers in the immediate foreground are drawn with great delicacy; so, too, is the fine foliage of the central tree. Between this tree and the one to the right of it a dramatic contrast is achieved.

17. Aix

Water-colour
Inscribed 'Lake of Aix from above Chambières'

A very pleasing mountain composition. An effect of calm

and grandeur is obtained by its dignified and restrained drawing. The floating clouds are very effective.

18. Cenis

Water-colour

Inscribed on mount 'Storm clouds on Cenis opposite St. Michael's Monastery'. On picture 'Rivoli Friday 13 Aug. 1858'

If the picture is seen at the right distance a vivid impression of a breaking cloud is obtained by the mass on the left of the drawing. The sense of mountain solitudes is conveyed by the whole picture.

19. Well at Camps near Abbeville

Ink, pencil, and water-colour

Inscribed 'Well at Camps near Abbeville'

An early drawing which shows in a remarkable degree Ruskin's power of rendering details in sympathetic spirit.

20. Study of Roofs

Water-colour

Here again his power to give a loving treatment of architectural details, showing the appeal they make to him, is seen. There was no intention here to do a picture, only faithfully to render these picturesque roofs.

21. Drawing of Ivy

Water-colour and pencil. 1879

Inscribed 'J. Ruskin Brantwood 1879'

A study of ivy in its natural environment. It conveys a sense of reality, for the ivy climbs naturally up the rock and is not on show.

22. Lucerne. Towers and hill

Water-colour

Inscribed 'Lucerne, Aug. 31st'. Some words in pencil are also written by Ruskin on the drawing, but are not legible.

An attractive drawing showing the beauty of the towers and their grouping.

23. Cloud effect over Coniston Old Man

Water-colour

The study of clouds was always a favourite one with Ruskin. This is a study of Coniston Old Man as seen in a storm from the windows of Brantwood. A little examination of the drawing will give the impression of storm-clouds playing about the mountain which is seen as a blue mass through the clouds.

24. Dieppe Cathedral

Pencil and wash

A slight but very delightful sketch. The care with which the upper part of the windows is drawn gives life to the picture.

25. St. Georges Crag

Water-colour

Inscribed '1. Ultra over pencil shadow
      2. Lake over all
      3. Raw sienna on lights only
      4. Ultram. over all
      5. Ult. stronger again over distant shadow, drawn in Spring 1881
      6. St. Georges Crag by 11 o'clock or noon about in Spring J. R. 5th Oct. 1881'

Also written by Ruskin in pencil on two of the hills 'Tiger', 'Eaglet'

Ruskin describes on this drawing the colours he has used

H

to get his effects, But he is anxious to portray the colour-effects as he saw them on the date and at the time given.

26. Mountain Scene, Pilatus, Lucerne
Water-colour

A very effective mountain study. The mountain stands out vividly with storm-clouds behind.

27. Rheinfelden
Ink, water-colour, and pencil. 1858
Inscribed 'Rheinfelden 1858. I never did nor shall do better. I think its violet carmine faded. J. Ruskin Brantwood 1879'

The town is shown in the plain with hills rising on each side. It is drawn with great sympathy, and the towers drawn at each corner at once enclose the town and give it unity and also give a protective feeling.

28. Domes and Sky (across the lagoons at Venice)
Water-colour

A vivid study in colour, probably by night. The domes and towers of Venice weird spectres amongst the clouds.

29. Study of Bay
Water-colour. 1882
Inscribed 'J. Ruskin 1882'

A careful, loving study showing the plant growing.

30. Study of Roofs
Water-colour and pencil

A very good example of the wonderful power Ruskin had of drawing a beautiful detail and conveying its appeal to the spectator. Note with what extreme care many of the windows are drawn in detail. In the background the outline of mountains is sketched in pencil.

31. Lucca Cathedral

Water-colour

Inscribed 'J. R. Lucca 30 Sept. 82. On Mount Lucca fast scrawl touched with colour. Drawn for the plan of composition of picture to be done by Henry Newman, who lost himself and me, alike, in his unhappy egotism of ultramarine —Rose Madda and Yellow Ochre—see unlucky drawing sent to Bewdley. J. R. 17 May 89'

This interesting drawing is reproduced in vol. xxxvii of the Library edition of Ruskin's works.

32. Ironwork at Verona

Water-colour

This ironwork is at the base of the Can Signorio tomb at Verona.

There are drawings of portions of this tomb in the galleries, Nos. 2 and 327, where fuller reference is made to the tomb.

The drawing is a most remarkable attempt to give the grace and beauty of the old ironwork. It is a good example of the care which Ruskin took to reproduce some vital feature of the work which he was engaged upon.

33. The Annunciation after Fra Angelico

Pencil

The galleries contain many examples of Ruskin's power when he copies pictures by old masters, but none more beautiful than this.

It is an exquisite drawing in pencil from Fra Angelico's lovely fresco at San Marco, Florence. The details of the archangel's robe could scarcely be done with greater fidelity and beauty. Look, too, at the hem of the Virgin's dress. Surely no pencil was ever more inspired!

34. Detail of the Castelbarco Tomb, Verona

Water-colour and wash

Inscribed 'Verona Tomb of Ct. Castelbarco J. Ruskin 1869'

A large water-colour drawing by Ruskin of this tomb is in the galleries (No. 65) and is described under that number in this book. This drawing of a detail of the tomb is done with dramatic vividness and is very effective in its impressionism.

35. Avallon, Details of Sculpture

Pencil and wash

Inscribed 'Like Sicilian. Four distinct incisions in mid leaf. Capital at Avallon 1882 J. R.'

Although only hastily done, these rough sketches show his never-failing study of minute detail.

36. Two Lions' Heads and a Tiger's Head

Water-colour and pencil

Sympathetic sketches showing humour and life.

37. Myrtilla Regina

Water-colour

Five sketches on three sheets of paper, one sheet containing three sketches.

The central sketch is reproduced in vol. xxv of the Library edition, Proserpina, plate xxiv.

Ruskin writes of it in *Proserpina*, 'Plate xxiv represents, however feebly, the proud bending back of her head by Myrtilla Regina, an action as beautiful in *her* as it is terrible in the kingly serpent of Egypt.'

Ruskin further describes this flower as arctostaphylos alpina, but suggests that he scarcely recognizes the flower in his botanical books. The other four sketches are apparently of the same flower. Underneath one of them he has written 'The real action and *will* of the flower'.

38. San Giovanni Eremita, Palermo

Pencil. 1874

Inscribed 'Palermo S. Giovanni Eremita 24 April 1874.
Inimitably lovely cloister capitals. The belfry window not
so much pointed as a failing normal arch yet evidently passing
into a point above, in the deep stone. Angle shafts with lovely
little caps like cloister'

Pencil sketches in which the main feature is the belfry
tower. The arches of one of the windows of the tower
are done with great care. The stonework is also vividly
suggested. Underneath the main drawing is an impression of one of the cloister capitals, which though very
hastily done conveys its beauty.

39. Haddon Hall

Pencil. 1837

Inscribed 'In the Gallery, Haddon, J. Ruskin 1837 signed
1880'

An example of his early pencil work, showing characteristic features. The drawing of the arch to the left of the
top windows is specially detailed.

40. Florence: Ponte Vecchio

Pencil

Signed 'John Ruskin' both in ink and in pencil

An exquisite example of Ruskin's work which was formerly in the possession of Lord Henry Bentinck. If the
drawing is examined from a little distance an extraordinarily successful mass effect is obtained. The space
beyond the arches of the bridge is suggested. The
picturesqueness of the houses on the bridge is conveyed
with great charm.

41. Melrose

Pencil with touches of ink and Chinese white. 1838

Inscribed 'The South Transept Melrose July 17 38'

Another very remarkable example of his early pencil work, this being done at the age of 19. The windows and doorway are drawn in great detail with wonderful fidelity. It will be found of great interest to look beyond the shafts of the great window on the right of the picture, when it will be realized that Ruskin has drawn the internal architecture of the room beyond. This little matter is really a revelation of the spirit in which Ruskin worked and taught.

42. Stirling Castle

Pencil. 1838

Inscribed 'Stirling 30th July 38. J. Ruskin Signed 28th Dec. 1879'

An early pencil drawing. The Castle itself is drawn with careful detail. The approach to it and the landscape is treated on broad and effective lines.

43. Rouen

Pencil

Inscribed 'Rouen'

A careful, interesting drawing showing on the left the great tower and on the right overhanging houses. The sketch belongs to his early period.

44. Rome

Ink, pencil, and wash

Inscribed 'S. Maria del Pianto, Roma'

An important drawing. A block of typical Roman houses is the most important part of the picture. In the foreground is a fountain. A number of people are sketched in. This is an unusual feature of Ruskin's drawings.

45. La Résidence, Munich

Pencil. 1835

Inscribed 'La Residence etc. Munich J. Ruskin 1835'

A wonderful drawing for a boy of 16. The exact and detailed work would be noteworthy if it were done by an artist of great experience. The drawing shows how quickly Ruskin perfected his own methods.

The drawing is also interesting because these formal buildings would not have attracted him at a later age.

The superb way in which the main doorway and the statuary on the façade are represented should be specially noticed. But every detail of this drawing is of great interest.

46. Calais

Ink

Inscribed 'Calais from the Sea. J. R.'

The drawing shows the towers of two churches and the tower of the lighthouse rising amid a sea of houses. There is a windmill on the right of the picture. A small sailing-boat on the sea at the left of the picture may be seen.

47. Fribourg

Ink

Inscribed 'Hotel de Ville, Fribourg J. R.'

A delightful example of Ruskin's work. It has a magical character, delicate and full of feeling. He combines with the most careful and exact detail the power of conveying the atmosphere of beauty. The buildings climb up the hill and culminate in the clock tower. The rocky foundations are shown.

There are two exquisite sketches shown in the distance

on the right of the picture. The one on the extreme right is of a church with tower, standing on a hill. The sense of space is admirably conveyed. The whole picture is a delight.

48. Street in St. Gall

Ink. 1835

An early sketch of the same character as No. 45. The overhanging windows on the left are wonderfully done. Ruskin gives a great dignity to the streets.

49. Amalfi

Pencil and wash. 1841

Inscribed 'Amalfi'

A most interesting example of his work. He was 22 when it was done. A magnificent mass of mountain is shown, and if the slopes of this are examined it will be seen with what care Ruskin has drawn numerous buildings and physical details. Note too the care with which the elaborate tower of the building in the foreground is done. This is reproduced in vol. xxxv of the Library edition, plate xvi.

50. Stuttgart

Pencil

Inscribed 'Der Stifts Kirch, Stutgard'

A very fine pencil drawing belonging to Ruskin's early period. A part of the church and two towers are shown. The care shown in this beautiful drawing could scarcely be exceeded. Note especially the doorway in the centre of the picture, the clock tower on the right. The gabled houses on the left of the picture are very attractive.

51. Richmond Market Place, Yorkshire

Pencil. 1838

Inscribed 'The Market Place, Richmond, Yorkshire
J. Ruskin 1838. Signed 28th Dec. 1879'

The title hardly describes this drawing, for the central
features are the church and tower. On the extreme right
is an obelisk with figures on the steps at its foot. There
are a few lonely stalls in the foreground. Ruskin rarely
introduced figures into his drawings.

52. Bristol

Pencil and Chinese white

Inscribed by Mrs. Severn 'Bristol by Di Pa given to me by
him 4th Jany 1886'

In the centre background are the beautiful tower and
church of St. Mary. In the foreground are three ships.
There is a small tower-like building to the right of the
church. There are two special points of interest in this
picture. One is the admirable composition in mass of the
church and tower. The other is the realistic drawing of
the ships.

53. Naples

Pencil and wash

Inscribed 'Naples'

The main feature is a domed church. There is a smaller
building in the foreground. On the right of the picture
there is an interesting group of buildings including a
castellated tower.

This is a photograph of the original which was given to
the Pope by the writer and is now in the Vatican Museum.

54. Benvenue

Pencil. 1838

Inscribed 'Benvenue, Trossacks over Achrig July 25th 38 J. Ruskin Signed Dec. 28 1879'

This drawing done at the age of 19 shows great skill in suggesting mountain masses. The nearer hills are shown in darker outline. The far shore of the lake is most pleasantly drawn. On the right is a road overhung with trees.

55. Tower in Richmond Castle, Yorkshire

Pencil. 1838

Inscribed 'Tower in Richmond Castle, Yorkshire, July 7th 38. J. Ruskin. Signed 7th Jan. 1880'

This is another early pencil drawing. It shows the ruined tower of the castle, and conveys the sympathy which Ruskin felt for great buildings of the past now in decay. Above the low wall on the left is a distant landscape.

56. Ponte Vecchio

Pencil and wash

Inscribed twice 'Ponte Vecchio Florence'

This drawing shows the view between the lines of houses and shops on the famous bridge. It is a difficult feat of composition. There is the same successful treatment of the mass combined with great attention to detail, as shown, for instance, in his drawings of the decorations on the side of the house on the left of the picture.

This is a photograph of the original which was given to the Italian nation by the author of this book and is now in the Capitoline Museum.

57. Mountain Study

Pencil

Inscribed 'J. Ruskin signed 7th January 1880'

A mountain peak, with trees in the foreground. The details of the rock formations of the peak are clearly indicated.

58. Near Zirl, Tyrol

Ink. 1835
Inscribed 'Near Zirl, Tyrol'

A very delicate mountain study. On the near hill what is probably a monastery is shown. The tower most effectively harmonizes with its surroundings. There is a second tower on a hill to the left. The figures of two peasants are seen in the right foreground. The trees in the centre of the foreground add to the beauty of this charming picture.

59. Merton College, Oxford

Pencil

A very careful and delightful architectural study. The tower is drawn with great sympathy and the details are given with great fidelity. Note particularly the pinnacles and arcading at the top of the tower, and the statue in a niche on the façade of the church, and the windows in the tower.

60. Cottage at Malham

Water-colour. 1876
Inscribed on the back, in the handwriting of Mrs. Arthur Severn, 'Highest House in England, Malham. By Di Pa'

There is a reference to this drawing in vol. 1, page 50, of the collected works, and it is reproduced in that volume. The cottage is in just such a position as Ruskin loved.

61. Drawing at Venice

Pencil and water-colour
Inscribed in Mrs. Arthur Severn's hand 'By J. R.'

A very interesting drawing, though unfinished. The

gothic arches on the buildings slightly to the left of the picture are rendered with Ruskin's habitual delicacy. The gondolas at their moorings at the left of the picture are effectively shown. On the right is a delicious cluster of growing flowers.

62. Ivy stems growing round the bough of a birch-tree

Water-colour

This drawing was apparently done in winter. It is an instance of Ruskin's care for detail. It shows with vividness the characteristics of the birch-tree.

63. Dover Castle

Pencil

Inscribed on back in Ruskin's handwriting 'Dover Castle from the west'

This is a very early drawing and was probably done by Ruskin at the age of 12. It shows all the characteristics of his early drawings, such as careful observation and intense devotion to the faithful rendering of details. It is a striking drawing for so young a boy. There is a courageous attempt by the treatment of clouds, sunlight, and rocks to give an impressive setting to the castle.

64. Palazzo Minischalchi, Verona

Water-colour

Initialled: J. R.

A fine drawing, showing doorway and windows above. The Gothic features are well brought out. Although the drawing is unfinished, especially at the foot, it is a most beautiful composition. The colours which Ruskin has used give the atmosphere of the building.

65. The Castelbarco Tomb, Verona

Water-colour

This large drawing is of great importance in showing the love which Ruskin felt for this tomb of Count Guglielino da Castelbarco erected in 1320. The tomb stands over the small cemetery gate of the Church of St. Anastasia at Verona. Ruskin describes it as 'the most perfect Gothic sepulchral monument in the world' (*Stones of Venice*, vol. 1) and makes frequent reference to it.

The following are special features of this very careful drawing. The arch on which the tomb stands is most beautifully drawn. Notice especially the realistic way in which the bricks on the right-hand side of the entrance are drawn. The tomb itself is given with great fidelity and the beauty of the arch above the tomb is shown with great sympathy. Ruskin described the construction of this arch in detail in vol. III of *The Stones of Venice*. This drawing is probably the 'careful plate' which he stated in *Modern Painters* he hoped to give of it (vol. 1, page 176, Library edition).

66. Architectural detail of arched windows for *The Stones of Venice*

Ink and wash

Inscribed 'Hexfoil window South Transept, St. Anastasia, Verona'

A fine unfinished drawing of a window in the South Transept of St. Anastasia, Verona.

67. Rouen

Pencil, pen, and wash

Inscribed 'Rouen J. R.'

A delicate and talented drawing obviously done when Ruskin was greatly influenced by Prout. The drawing shows old gabled houses with a tower rising behind.

68. The Castle at Annecy

Four impressions from the plate, namely original impression, two progress proofs worked by Ruskin, and final proof

Ruskin refers to this work in *Praeterita*, vol. II (Library edition, vol. xxxv, page 344), in the following words:

'At Annecy I made the first careful trial of my new way of work. I herewith reproduce the study; it is very pleasant to me still; and certainly any artist who once accustoms himself to the method cannot afterwards fall into any mean trickery or dull conventionalism. The outline must be made clearly and quietly, conveying as much accurate information as possible respecting the form and structure of the object; then, in washing, the chiaroscuro is lowered from the high lights with extreme care down to the middle tones, and the main masses left in full shade.'

The final proof is reproduced in the Library edition, vol. xxxv, plate XXII.

69. Roslin Chapel

Pencil, very slightly touched with white paint
Inscribed 'Roslin Chapel Aug. 3 38'

This is a remarkably interesting drawing. It was made when Ruskin was 19 years old and shows his splendid powers of draughtsmanship even as a youth. The details of roof, windows, capitals, indeed every part of the drawing, deserve the most careful study.

70. Copy of Veronese's The Cuccina Family (Dresden)

Pencil, ink, and water-colour

This is a copy of a part of Veronese's picture, The Cuccina Family, now at Dresden. It was a favourite picture of Ruskin's and he makes a number of references to it in several of his works. He thus describes it in the last volume of *Modern Painters*, Library edition, vol. VII, pages 290 ff.:

'The picture most illustrative of this feeling[1] is perhaps that at Dresden, of Veronese's family, painted by himself.

'He wishes to represent them as happy and honoured. The best happiness and highest honour he can imagine for them is that they should be presented to the Madonna, to whom, therefore, they are being brought by the three Virtues—Faith, Hope, and Charity.

'The Virgin stands in a recess behind two marble shafts, such as may be seen in any house belonging to an old family in Venice. She places the boy Christ on the edge of a balustrade before her. At her side are St. John the Baptist and St. Jerome. This group occupies the left side of the picture. The pillars, seen sideways, divide it from the group formed by the Virtues, with the wife and children of Veronese. He himself stands a little behind, his hands clasped in prayer.

'His wife kneels full in front, a strong Venetian woman, well advanced in years. She has brought up her children in fear of God, and is not afraid to meet the Virgin's eyes. She gazes steadfastly on them; her proud head and gentle, self-possessed face are relieved in one broad mass of shadow against a space of light, formed by the white robes of Faith, who stands beside her—guardian and companion. Perhaps a somewhat disappointing Faith at the first sight, for her face is not in any special way exalted or refined. Veronese knew that Faith had to companion simple and slow-hearted people, perhaps oftener than able or refined people—does not therefore insist on her being severely intellectual, or looking as if she were always in the best company. So she is only distinguished by her pure white

[1] That is to say, the truth expressed by some painters that to show children playing in the presence of Christ was natural and right.

(not bright white) dress, her delicate hand, her golden hair drifted in light ripples across her breast, from which the white robes fall nearly in the shape of a shield—the shield of Faith. A little behind her stands Hope; she also, at first, not to most people a recognizable Hope. We usually paint Hope as young and joyous. Veronese knows better. The young Hope is vain Hope—passing away in rain of tears; but the Hope of Veronese is aged, assured, remaining when all else has been taken away. "For tribulation worketh patience, and patience experience, and experience hope"; and *that* hope maketh not ashamed.

'She has a black veil on her head.

'Then again, in the front, is Charity, red-robed; stout in the arms—a servant of all work, she; but small-headed, not being specially given to thinking; soft-eyed, her hair braided brightly; her lips rich red, sweet-blossoming. She has got some work to do even now, for a nephew of Veronese's is doubtful about coming forward, and looks very humbly and penitently towards the Virgin—his life perhaps not having been quite so exemplary as might at present be wished. Faith reaches her small white hand lightly back to him, lays the tips of her fingers on his; but Charity takes a firm hold of him by the wrist from behind, and will push him on presently, if he still hangs back.

'In front of the mother kneel her two eldest children, a girl of about sixteen, and a boy a year or two younger. They are both rapt in adoration—the boy's being the deepest. Nearer us, at their left side, is a younger boy, about nine years old—a black-eyed fellow, full of life—and evidently his father's darling (for Veronese has put him full in light in the front; and given him a beautiful white silken jacket, barred with black, that nobody may ever miss seeing him to the end of time). He is a little shy about being presented to the Madonna, and for the present has got behind the pillar, blushing, but opening his black eyes wide; he is just summoning courage to peep round and see if she looks kind. A still younger child, about six years old, is really frightened, and has run back to his mother, catching hold of her dress at the waist. She throws her right arm round him and over him, with exquisite instinctive action, not moving her eyes from the Madonna's face. Last of all, the youngest child, perhaps about three years old, is neither frightened nor interested, but finds the ceremony tedious, and is trying to coax the dog to play with him; but the dog, which is one of the little curly, short-nosed, fringy-pawed things, which all Venetian ladies petted, will not now be coaxed.'

71. Detail from Veronese's The Cuccina Family (Dresden)

Pencil and wash

This is an unfinished drawing of the head of the boy who is seen on the extreme left of the previous drawing. It enables the great charm of the original picture to be fully realized.

72. Copy of Botticelli's Zipporah's Flock (Sistine Chapel, Rome)

Water-colour

This is a very charming drawing of a detail of Botticelli's fresco in the Sistine Chapel at Rome. There is an extraordinary distinctiveness shown in this drawing and it reproduces with great fidelity Botticelli's work in the fresco. If the picture is examined with care the observer will get a sense of extraordinary harmony in the lines of the animals and the landscape. The tree, too, is very interesting and beautiful.

K

73. Copy of Dog by Carpaccio (Venice)
Water-colour

This is another example of Ruskin's patience and skill in copying the works of great masters. There is a distinct touch of humour in the drawing of the dog. The detail is taken from Carpaccio's picture.

74. Wall-Veil Decoration, with the final engraving from it
Water-colour and pencil

This is one of the numerous drawings Ruskin made for *The Stones of Venice*, in which work it is reproduced, vol. I, plate XXII. It is a very delicate drawing in which every detail is given. The simple beauty of the decoration which Ruskin was copying is revealed to those who have never seen the original.

75. Map of Turkey in Europe
Water-colour and pencil

This is one of the many maps which Ruskin did as a child. The training which he gave himself in map-drawing when so young was a great help to the development of his draughtsmanship.

76. Venetian Decorative Carving
Pencil

This is one of the drawings which Ruskin did to illustrate the architecture of Venice.

77. Venetian Capital
Pencil

Another of Ruskin's drawings to illustrate the architecture of Venice.

78. Copy of Tintoretto's Adoration of the Magi
Water-colour

Ruskin's admiration for Tintoretto is well known; he could not have shown it more clearly than in making this copy. It is unfinished but is in every way a great success and great achievement. The splendid decorative spirit of the original work is preserved. Nothing could be better than the figures of the Virgin and of the Magi. Tintoretto's great quality of being able to give the impression of life to the characters of his canvas is shown in this copy. There is nothing unreal or formal about the woman with the basket, and the other characters, whether principal or secondary. Everything in the picture is living and joyous.

79. Detail from Tintoretto's Adoration of the Magi

This is a preliminary sketch of part of the Adoration of the Magi. It shows how carefully Ruskin worked on his copies of these great masters.

80. Detail from Tintoretto's Adoration of the Magi

A preliminary sketch in pencil of the central figure of the Magi for the water-colour described above, No. 78. The central figure, though only lightly sketched in pencil, is a very remarkable copy of Tintoretto's picture in oils.

81. Copy of one of the Daughters of Jethro in Botticelli's fresco in the Sistine Chapel, Rome
Water-colour

This is a very remarkable drawing and should be compared with the complete fresco by Botticelli from which it is taken. Ruskin has been extremely successful in drawing the very beautiful face which conveys the genius of Botticelli in a very remarkable way. The eyes are most wonderfully done. The dress is exquisitely painted, particularly the borders, which are given with faithful detail. The picture is a monument in itself to Ruskin's indefatigable industry.

82. Copy of part of Tintoretto's Crucifixion (Venice)

Ink and wash

This is a copy of the central portion of Tintoretto's great picture at Venice and shows Christ upon the Cross. It is drawn with great realism.

83. Neuchâtel

Pencil

Inscribed 'Neuchatel sketched 1863 I think invaluable now for the lines of roof of old town (call this Neuchatel B and C)'

One of the numerous drawings Ruskin made for use in subsequent studies and writings. The student should always remember that the inscriptions on Ruskin's drawings were generally written years after the drawings were made, as in this case.

84. Two Maps of Arabia

Water-colour

Two good examples of Ruskin's maps in colour.

85. Map showing the physical geography of Palestine

Water-colour

The colour effect obtained is realistic.

86. Map of Italy

Water-colour

Inscribed 'My first map of Italy'

A delightful little map done by Ruskin when a child.

87. Abbeville Cathedral
Water-colour and pencil

Only the roof, tower, and buttresses are completed. The remainder is roughly sketched in pencil. The picture is an illustration of Ruskin's habit of drawing details of buildings for various purposes.

88. River Scene
Pen and ink, and wash

With very simple means Ruskin has got a most pleasing result. Trees and buildings are in the distance. The reflections in the water are effectively done.

89. Grand Canal, Venice
Pencil, with some white

Ruskin's love of the Grand Canal was great. He made a number of sketches of it, of which this is an example. He has lavished great care on the houses on the left. The drawing is at once architectural and imaginative. The details are wonderfully rendered.

90. S. N. de Tolentini
Pencil
Inscribed 'S. N. de Tolentini 31 Dec 76 J Ruskin'

91. Camareggio, Venice
Pencil
Inscribed 'Camareggio, Venice January 77 J Ruskin'

92. Rialto
Pencil
Inscribed 'Rialto J. Ruskin Dec. 1876'

93. Rialto
Pencil
Inscribed 'Rialto January 77 J Ruskin'

94. Venice
Pencil

Inscribed 'Venice Feb. 77 J. Ruskin'

The above five drawings are in one frame. They are illustrative of the careful studies Ruskin made of every part of Venice. These were made towards the close of the active years of his life, but they show his interest and powers undimmed.

95. Snowclad Mountains
Water-colour

The blue and white effects are very beautifully obtained in the distant mountains. The power of contrast is obtained by the way in which he has drawn the foreground in relation to the distant hills.

96. Wellhorn and Wetterhorn
Ink and Chinese white

Inscribed 'Wellhorn and Wetterhorn from the banks of the Reichenbach. John Ruskin'

Probably an early mountain sketch with Turner-like touches. Ruskin has made a special feature of the tree in the foreground. A stag looks at the water from the rocky banks overlooking the stream. The distant houses and other details are delicately rendered.

97. Portrait of Ruskin by himself
Pencil

This drawing was formerly in the possession of Ruskin's friend C. E. Norton. It is a portrait of Ruskin drawn by himself in the year 1874. It was done for his friend Charles Eliot Norton of Boston. On February 15, 1874, Ruskin wrote to Norton from Corpus Christi College,

Oxford, saying, 'I shall make you a little drawing of myself positively before I go abroad.' On April 9 of the same year he writes again to him from Pisa: 'I have told Burgess to send you the two beginnings of myself I made for you. All that is good in me depends upon terrible subtleties, which I find will require my very best care and power of completion—all that comes at first is the worst. Continually I see accidental looks, which, if I could set down, you would like . . . only I let these failures be sent to show I have been trying.' This drawing is one of those to which Ruskin refers. It remained, unpublished, in the possession of Professor Norton until his death, when it passed to his son. It was sold at Christie's in May 1919.

98. Mountains

Water-colour. 1845

Inscribed on back, 'By John Ruskin given by him to me Joan Ruskin Severn.' On front, 'Rothhorn and Arret Blanche from approach to Sisto Calande. Oct 21st 45 J. R.'

A very beautiful study of mountains, the sky with its red flickers of cloud is most charmingly rendered.

99. Historical Maps of France

Pencil, ink, and wash

Five maps which formed the basis of those which appeared in the Bible of Amiens. (See plate VI in vol. XXXIII of the Library edition, where they are reproduced under the title of 'The Dynasties of France to the close of the Tenth Century'.)

100. Map of North America

Ink and water-colour

Done by Ruskin as a child.

101. Mountain village

Water-colour

Inscribed on back 'by John Ruskin. Given by him to me Joan Ruskin Severn'

A very charming drawing of an Italian mountain village; the houses amid their settings of trees and mountains are most beautifully drawn.

102. Map of Spain and Portugal

Ink and water-colour

This and No. 100 are examples of the maps done by Ruskin as a child.

103. Cloud Study

Water-colour

Inscribed by Arthur Severn 'This may be published. Ruskin quite approves'

104. Cloud Study

Water-colour

Bearing a similar inscription by Arthur Severn to No. 103. These two drawings are typical of the skill with which Ruskin dealt with cloud effects. A fine Turneresque impression is given.

105. Soldiers Fighting

Ink

Inscribed 'Soldiers fighting' and initialled 'J. R.'

A drawing from an old bas-relief.

106. Venice. Stilted archivolts. From a ruin in the Rio di Ca' Foscari

Water-colour

This drawing is reproduced in the Library edition of Ruskin's works, in *The Stones of Venice*.

107. Bridge, Lauffenbourg

Water-colour, pencil, and ink. 1863.

Inscribed 'Under bridge of Lauffenbourg, Lauffenbourg 1863'

An interesting drawing; the details of the bridge are carefully given, and the swirling water is well drawn.

108. Peacock's Feather
Falcon's Feather

Water-colour

These drawings were made by Ruskin for his Oxford lectures on birds. The peacock's feather is specially interesting, the blue colouring being given with great beauty and the structure of the feather made very clear.

109. Lucca: Drawing of a Shield

Water-colour

The quarterings of the shield are shown in red with heraldic decoration on the white cross.

110. Map of Africa

Outlined in water-colour

Inscribed at foot 'John Ruskin Oct. 11th 1830'

Ruskin was 11 years old when he did this map. It is most carefully drawn, and the names of the places are written with extreme care and neatness. It is obviously a map which gave him a great deal of pleasure to make. This is one of a number of maps which Ruskin made, and of which there are seven others in this collection.

111. St. Raniez

Pencil, ink, and water-colour

Inscribed at foot, on mount: 'I drew it for the sake of the

L

leaf ground. I have just touched with ink which I have
got to. First sketch of mine in 1845 from (Simone Memmi?)
Life of St. Raniez in Campo Santo of Pisa. It has got the
expression of the principal figure a little on its purple ground,
and has something of the grace of the lines. The figures
were out of drawing in the original—of course got worse in
mine. J. Ruskin 1868'

Ruskin's own words on the mount of this picture, which
are quoted above, explain this sketch. It is done with great
care. There is much delicacy and beauty in the composition of this drawing. The figure on the left, of which
Ruskin has almost completed the face, is most interesting.

112. Carved Lion

Water-colour

Inscribed 'You know where this is. Keep it for yourself.
J.R. 1879'

This drawing was sent by Ruskin to his friend Charles
Eliot Norton.

113. Mountain-side and Lake, Lucerne

Water-colour

A beautiful drawing at sunset. There is an effective contrast between the sky on the left of the drawing and the
colours of the hills.

114. A Vineyard walk at Lucca. The lower stonework of Tower: 12th century

Water-colour

The drawing shows a road between walls and hills and
gardens. The central feature of interest is the tower and
old wall in the centre of the picture. Immediately to the
right of the tower there are charming light-effects. It is
a characteristic example of Ruskin's work, with most

careful finish of the features he wished to emphasize.
See, for example, the stonework half-way up the tower.

Reproduced in vol. xxxvii, page 126, Library edition.

115. The Mountains of Villeneuve

Water-colour

This drawing is reproduced by an engraving in vol. iv of
Modern Painters (Library edition, vol. vi, page 301).

Ruskin says of it, 'Plate 40 opposite represents a mass
of mountains which is above Villeneuve at the head of the
Lake of Geneva in which the type of the structure is shown
with singular clearness. Much of the scenery of Western
Switzerland and characteristically the whole of that of
Savoy is composed of mountains of this kind.'

116. Architectural Details at Assisi

Pencil, wash, and water-colour

Inscribed, 'Assisi—characteristic. The narrower stones
naturally resulting from convenient weights for masons to
lift'

(The above inscription relates to the arch at the top of the
picture.)

The other inscriptions on different details are:

'Relative size of rolls right.'

(The above refers to the drawing of stones to the left
of the arch.)

'Assisi on another key stone.'

(This refers to the carved cross on the lower left-hand
side of the drawing.)

'Walls all squares. Three shields like this. The wide
chequers painted on marble. Wall of suppressed church
of San Francisco de' Conventuali at Perugia.'

These drawings of details are a good example of the
detailed work which Ruskin did at many little-known
buildings.

117. Four sketches of Details of Venetian Buildings

Pencil and wash

The lower middle sketch is inscribed 'Ca' Saguedo. A is the central capital. The sides of B both alike. C a bit of fresco.'

There are a number of pencil notes on the upper middle drawing.

118. Swallows' nests

Pencil and wash

Inscribed 'Sketch for a lesson in chiaroscuro. Bracket with swallows' nests old English. Timber lych. Thame, Berkshire. J. Ruskin 1873'

The tiles on the left are well given, although the sketch is obviously a hasty one. The nests with their entrances can be seen just above the bracket.

119. Two drawings of common Marsh Thistle

Water-colour and ink

The drawing is in two parts, and each is signed John Ruskin. These sketches when carefully examined show the amazing faithfulness with which he has drawn this common feature of the country-side.

120. Map of Scotland

Ink and water-colour. 1828

Inscribed 'March 27 John Ruskin aged nine 1828'

This singularly interesting map by Ruskin was done at the age of nine. It shows all the loving interest in the faithful recording of detail which is common to all his work. It is a remarkable map for a boy of nine to have done.

121. View from Bonneville

Water-colour and pencil

A little drawing with the mountains partly outlined in pencil. It gives by very simple means a good idea of the beautiful position of the town.

122. Verona

Pencil

Inscribed 'Verona J. R. 1872'

The chief feature of this hasty drawing is the gothic house on the left side of the road. Although obviously a rapid sketch, the character of the central buildings, at the bases of which there are gothic arches, is clearly indicated.

123. Detail of leaf design

Pencil

A very careful drawing of a piece of sculpture based upon leaf design.

124. Details from the Badia of Fiesole

Water-colour. 1874

An admirable drawing which reproduces the atmosphere of the stone pillars very effectively. Note, too, the little details of sculpture in the bottom left-hand corner, and the drawing of a plant at the foot of the picture.

125. Roses from Botticelli

Water-colour

A copy of one of the sprays of roses on the dress of the central figure in Botticelli's 'Spring'. It is a remarkable copy, and when it is remembered that this is one tiny detail of a great picture it enables us to realize the patient genius of Botticelli. Note especially the way the leaves are drawn and the opening bud on the right of the picture.

126. Capital, Ducal Palace, Venice

Wash, pencil, and ink

This drawing of one of the Ducal Palace capitals representing Justice is one of a great number of Ruskin's architectural studies in Venice. It is, I suppose, a far greater thing to be able to draw faithfully a carving in stone and to give a faithful impression of the original than to make a copy of another drawing. Certainly no one has surpassed Ruskin in his power of drawing architectural details of this kind.

127. St. Andrea, Venice

Pencil and wash

Inscribed 'St. Andrea 17 Feb 77'

This drawing was formerly in the possession of Mr. Albert Flemming, who has written on the back the following note: 'This original drawing of the Church of St. Andrea was made by Mr. Ruskin in Venice in 1877, and given by him to me in May 1886. It has to me an added value as being one of the last things my dear friend Mrs. Hobart cared to see. She was then lying in the shadow of death, but instantly recognised this little drawing, and referred to the grassy plateau in part of it. It is scarcely an adequate example of Mr. Ruskin's skill, but is valuable for its sense of proportion and curious in its splendid swiftness and care, six of the perpendicular lines being ruled with precision, all the rest worked in freely. A. F. July 86.'

128. Venice

Water-colour and pencil

Inscribed 'Venice (Con. D. Guidecia Sept. 13)'

A distant sketch of Venice done apparently at evening time. There is a break in the clouds and the colour effects on the water are suggested. It is a pleasing, vivid impression.

129. Mountain Study

Water-colour

A characteristic drawing of mountains, probably in Switzerland. It is a realistic sketch, and the impressiveness of the mountains is well conveyed. On the back of this drawing is a study of clouds and water.

130. Drawings of Details of the Ducal Palace, Venice

These drawings are on two sheets. The upper sheet is inscribed by Ruskin: 'Part of Renaissance Balconies, Ducal Palace', and shows quite extraordinarily interesting patterns in stone of the balconies.

Two similar sketches on this sheet show the rope-like effect of the intertwining of the stone.

The lower sheet is inscribed 'Main cornice side C', and contains fourteen sketches in pencil.

131. Pays de Vaud, near Bex

Ink. 1835

This drawing was done by Ruskin when he was 16 years old. Note especially the treatment of the tree on the left of the drawing. It is realistic and effective.

132. Entrance to Battle Abbey

Pencil

This is a very early drawing by Ruskin when a boy. It

is most carefully done, and the line of arches above the entrance is worthy of special notice.

133. Sketch at Rheinfelden
Ink and pencil

A small but exquisite sketch. Even a much larger one could scarcely have given beautiful details in a more loving manner than this. It is an old cottage apparently on the summit of a hill, enclosed by a high wall.

134. The Monument in St. Eustagio, Milan
This sketch shows in a little detail the upper part of the monument.

135. Monument in St. Eustagio
Pencil

Inscribed 'Monument in St. Eustagio Milan 1862'

This is a hasty drawing of two of the animals which adorn the monument.

136. Building at Bienne
Inscribed 'Middle tower with its shadow on house roof. Bienne. C. 1859'

A very slight but interesting sketch showing Ruskin's close observation of the smallest details.

137. Venetian Gondola
Water-colour

This is a study of the gondola which appears in a large drawing done by Ruskin in 1876 of Casa Foscari and the Frari.

138. Village on a hill
Water-colour

A study chiefly of the roadway, and of the village houses,

with the church on the right-hand side. Ruskin was showing the beauty of the effect of this little cluster of houses, and he indicates the beauty of the detail by showing with great exactitude a little group of trees at the side of the church.

139. A shell
Water-colour

This is a carefully executed drawing, and gives in a most realistic way the texture of the shell. It is a patient drawing, and although the subject would not appeal perhaps to many, it shows the genius which Ruskin had for rendering every object in which he was interested with great fidelity.

140. Neuchâtel
Pencil

Inscribed 'Neuchatel. To lake from castle'

On the reverse is a rough pencil drawing of a line of trees.

141. Detail of Sculpture at Avallon
Water-colour

A rapid sketch giving an unusual form in stone carving.

142. Ducal Palace. Sketches of four capitals
Pencil and wash

An example of a vast number of careful drawings which Ruskin did, of these and similar details, at Venice.

143. Study of Drapery
Pencil and wash

There is a note on the back of this picture in Fairfax Murray's handwriting stating that this was done at Burne-Jones's house in August 1868.

M

144. Carlisle Cathedral

Pencil

Inscribed 'J. Ruskin signed 7 Jan 1880 Carlisle Cathedral August VII xxxviii'

It was Ruskin's custom to sign his pictures many years after they had been drawn, which accounts for the two dates in this instance. The drawing is an early one and shows the mastery which he had obtained at an early age in rendering the most delicate detail in pencil. The canopies over the walls deserve careful study.

145. Mill at Eaton Bedford

Pencil

Inscribed 'Mill at Eaton Bedford J. Ruskin 1837. Signed December 28th 1879'

A very pleasing drawing. The details are admirably done. Notice, for instance, the plant growing out of the water on the left of the picture, and in the foreground at the foot of the picture. This mill, with its broken roofs and dormer windows and timber work, would naturally attract Ruskin.

146. Lago di Sarola

Pencil heightened with white

Inscribed 'Lago di Sarola J. Ruskin 1835'

This is one of a large number of sketches which Ruskin did as a youth under the influence of Turner. It at once recalls vignettes in Rogers's *Italy*.

147. Castelbarco Tomb

Water-colour

A detail done with admirable colouring.

148. Inlaid Marbles for *The Stones of Venice*

Water-colour

This is a remarkable drawing showing Ruskin's extraordinary success in giving a life-like study of the various stones which he has drawn.

It is reproduced in *The Stones of Venice*, Library edition, vol. IX, page 33, and is described as Wall Veil Decoration: Ca' Trevisan and Ca' Dario.

149. Ochils

Pencil. 1838

Inscribed 'Ochils from Stirling J. Ruskin 1838 Signed 28 December 1879'

The early drawings by Ruskin, of which this is a very fine example, show the remarkable standard which he had reached at a very early age. This drawing with its distant mountains and buildings and pool in the near foreground is successful not only for the accuracy of its drawing but also for its remarkable composition.

150. St. Mary Magdalene, Oxford

Pencil. 1836

Inscribed 'St. Mary Magdalene Oxford John Ruskin 1837. Signed 1880 J. Ruskin'

It is interesting to see that in these early drawings Ruskin had already adopted the practice which he maintained throughout his life of drawing with extraordinary fidelity and care such details of buildings as appealed to him, or which he wished to record for some special purpose. In this picture the ruined angle of the building is sketched with almost photographic exactitude.

151. Hôtel de Ville, Cassel

Pencil. 1833

Inscribed 'Hotel de Ville Cassel'

This drawing is of unusual interest, for it is the first sketch which Ruskin made on the Continent. He was 14 years of age when he did it.

The building on the left has a fine central doorway. The boy artist has forgotten nothing in this sketch. There is no attempt to give an impression. Everything is shown. Note the step arrangement on the gable at the top of the picture on the left. Note too the way in which the ornamentation is given between the ground-floor windows and the first-floor windows.

A most interesting drawing.

152. Mont Righi and the Burnese Alps
Pencil

Inscribed 'Mont Righi and the Burnese Alps over the Lake of Zug. J. Ruskin 1835. Signed 1880'

A drawing in the spirit of Turner. The mountain, shore, and lake with a little house on the left of the picture make a wonderful harmony.

153. Bridge at Venice
Water-colour

A delightful water-colour. On the left are houses with balconies, and gothic windows. In the centre is a bridge over a canal. Beyond the bridge are other houses, and the higher portion of a campanile. On the right-hand side of the picture there is what appears to be an old wooden post rising from the water. It is drawn with great fidelity.

154. Watendlath Tarn, Cumberland
Pencil

Inscribed 'Watendlath Tarn Cumberland August 16 38. John Ruskin signed 7 Jan 1880'

A fine pencil drawing of hills, lake and bridge. It should be noted that many of Ruskin's drawings give us most valuable records of bridges and cottages which have long since perished. This is a good example.

155. Village, Lake, and Mountain

Inscribed 'J. Ruskin 1835'

Another Turneresque drawing of great delicacy. The central feature of this sketch is the village on the shores of the lake, and Ruskin shows his mastery of composition in his treatment of the buildings.

156. Chapel of St. John, Genoa Cathedral

Pencil heightened with white. 1840

Inscribed 'Chapel of St. John Duomo Genoa Sketch in 1840. Signed 1882. John Ruskin'

A delicate architectural work. On the left side of the picture is a very carefully drawn statue, apparently of St. John holding a cross, with a richly adorned canopy above. The distances in the cathedral are well suggested by the distant group on the right of the picture.

157. Brick Archivolt

Water-colour

This is a most beautifully finished drawing, and is reproduced in *The Stones of Venice*. The details of the upper arch are given with supreme skill. The lower arch is also very beautifully done.

158. Mill, probably at Troutbeck

Pencil

Inscribed 'Mill Troutbeck? J. Ruskin 1838 signed 1880'

An early drawing. When he examined this drawing later, Ruskin was uncertain as to where it was made.

It is a picturesque little sketch. The old wheel is shown with water pouring from it. To the right of the wheel there is a tiny bridge over the stream.

159. St. Gotthard. The lowest bridge on the north side

Pencil and water-colour

Inscribed 'St. Gotthard. Lowest bridge coming down on north side. Valley of Altorf down under distant peaks. Sketched in Wisie's time. Lily saying she wished she could outline like that'

Though slight, this sketch shows the remarkable charm of Ruskin's outlines.

160. Mountain scene

Pencil

Inscribed 'Scene from the top of the Stelvio looking towards the Italian side. J. Ruskin 1835'

A sketch made at the age of 16 in his Turneresque manner.

161. Mer de Glace from the Montanvert

Water-colour

A superb mountain study. Ruskin suggests the glorious colouring of the rocks in the foreground with the ice and snow of the more distant peaks.

This drawing is reproduced in vol. xxvi of the Library edition, plate A, page xxii.

162. John of Bologna, Casa Cecchi, Borgo S. Jacopo

Pencil and wash

Inscribed 'John of Bologna Casa Cecchi Ospezio dei Borgo S. Jacopo J. R.'

This is a very interesting drawing even apart from the statue in the foreground. The distant winding street is specially attractive, and it is unusual to find many of Ruskin's drawings containing human figures.

163. Head of Solomon from Paolo Veronese

Water-colour

A very fine copy of the head from Veronese's picture. To see this drawing to the best advantage, the student should stand a few yards away. He will then realize the beautiful treatment of the eye, and the general expression of the face.

164. Loch Katrine

Pencil

Inscribed 'Loch Katrine looking to Coir near Uriston July 28 38. J. Ruskin signed 28 December 1879'

Another of the delightful series of sketches which Ruskin made in England and Scotland in his youth.

The mountains are impressively shown rising above the lake.

165. On the Reuss near Altorf

Ink

The drawing is inscribed as above title, and initialled by Ruskin.

A very careful drawing of a châlet on the shores of the lake, with a distant view of mountains.

166. Church at Bienne

Pencil

Inscribed 'Bienne B Middle bit in Bienne A'

A slight pencil sketch which should be examined in connexion with the other sketches at Bienne. (See Nos. 204 and 272.)

167. Bonneville from Turner's Drawing

Pencil

Inscribed 'Pencil study from Turner's Bonneville J R 1873'

This unfinished sketch from Turner is very delicately done, and shows a most successful rendering of the mountain masses.

168. A Jackal

Pencil and crayon

Inscribed 'British Museum stuffed Jackal J.R. 1872'

Ruskin made many studies of animals and birds from time to time at the British Museum.

169. Lauffenbourg

Pencil

Inscribed 'Laufenberg J. R. 1862'

This slight drawing shows the bridge across the river.

170. Matlock

Pencil

Inscribed 'J R Matlock June 1871'

Ruskin was very successful in being able to give realistic mass effects in pencil.

171. Capital of a column drawn from *The Stones of Venice*

Water-colour

This is one of numerous drawings of architectural details which Ruskin made. He was always fascinated by these architectural details, and was never tired of drawing them.

172. Study in France

Water-colour and pencil

A public building, probably in France. I have not been able to identify the building yet. It shows the influence of Prout. It is not quite so clear in detail as many of his architectural drawings are. This is apparently due to the wash which he has used. It is a drawing which demanded great patience. It is impressive and, seen at a little distance, the composition is most harmonious.

173. Architectural detail, St. Mark's, Venice
Pencil

This is one of the sculptures above a window in St. Mark's, showing, apparently, one of the apostles in the act of blessing.

In addition to the careful figure drawing, Ruskin has indicated the character of the carved borders.

174. St. Mary's Tower, Carlisle Castle
Pencil

Inscribed 'Mary's Tower, Carlisle Ca June 28 1837. Signed December 28th 1879'

An early drawing, but, like nearly all his architectural drawings in youth, done with great care. The gothic stonework is rendered with great fidelity.

175. The Spanish Chapel, Florence
Water-colour

A very rapid drawing of the frescoes on one of the walls.

176. St. Mark's, Venice
Water-colour

This is a magnificent example of Ruskin's architectural drawing. It is, of course, only a very small detail of the interior of St. Mark's, but yet it shows a wonderful variety of arches. Notice the capitals of the columns in the lower part of the picture, then the way in which the columns of varying stones are shown above. In the dome in the top right corner of the picture are some examples of the mosaics of St. Mark's. The arch on the right, underneath the dome, is shown in great detail.

Such a drawing is of very great importance to the student unable to visit St. Mark's, or who, having visited it, desires to have some of its contents interpreted.

N

177. Pass of St. Gotthard, near Amsteg

Pen and Ink

Inscribed 'Near Amsteg, Pass of St. Gotthard'

An early drawing, with Ruskin's usual characteristics. In the foreground there is a bridge. In the distance, and to the right of it, are mountains. Ruskin quite clearly suggests the valley before the mountains, near the bridge, and the distant ones. On the right of the picture some typical mountain buildings are indicated.

178. Sculptured Heads at Amiens Cathedral

Pencil

One of Ruskin's numerous drawings at Amiens. It is a careful study of sculptured heads. This drawing should be compared with No. 207, in which the same heads are drawn, but in greater detail.

179. Ponte Vecchio, Florence

Water-colour

This is a delightful view of part of this famous bridge. Ruskin was always interested in this bridge, and a pencil drawing is shown in the collection, No. 40. As in the other drawing of the bridge the composition is very effective.

180. Arches

Pencil

This is a very slight sketch near the Ponte Vecchio, Florence.

181. Study from Luini, at Milan

Water-colour

182. Sailing-boats at Venice

Water-colour

Ruskin was very fond of drawing Venetian boats and gondolas, and these are characteristic notes.

183. St. Martin's, opposite Sallenche

Water-colour

A very charming drawing. Although the size is so small, the details are rendered with extraordinary fidelity and realism. Only a painter with very good eyesight could have drawn this. Notice, for example, the way in which the broken slates are shown on the roof, the little creepers growing up the building in the foreground, and the row of pillars.

184. Chartres Cathedral

Water-colour

An unfinished drawing of Chartres. In the background is the Cathedral with its spire; in the foreground, Ruskin has begun to paint the roofs of a house.

185. Wooden angel

Water-colour

Inscribed 'Wooden angel with face broken off Chartres'

The drawing shows a very graceful wooden statue, the wings of the angel being designed with great beauty. The folds of the angel's dress are suggested with great effectiveness.

186. Study of a chair by Carpaccio

Water-colour. 1876

A rather gorgeous little drawing in red of the chair in Carpaccio's 'St. Jerome', San Giorgio de' Schiavoni, Venice.

187. Giotto's Tower, Florence

Water-colour

These are two drawings of the panels in the great tower. Ruskin has written exhaustively on the subject, particularly in *Mornings in Florence*.

188. Spanish Chapel, Florence

Pencil and water-colour

This is a copy from one of the frescoes in the chapel, the subject of which is Grammar directing one of her scholars through the strait gate.

189. Architectural Drawings, Venice

Three drawings are shown in this frame, each of great interest. The larger shows a beautiful gothic arch enclosing windows. The second in size shows details of gothic windows; and the smallest drawing shows details of the stonework.

These drawings show, as do hundreds of others, Ruskin's infinite capacity for drawing details to set forth the exact truth of what he was describing.

190. Capital, Venice

Pencil and water-colour

A most admirable study for *The Stones of Venice*. The details of the sculptured capital are most wonderfully done.

191. Interior of St. Mark's, Venice

Water-colour

This picture is a remarkable example of Ruskin's power in rendering with great fidelity details whether in art or in architecture. The drawing shows some of the mosaics in St. Mark's, consisting of four groups of personages.

Above are shown the interior of some of the domes, and
other details of the Cathedral. The drawing reproduces
in a wonderful way the atmosphere of the building. The
expressions of the characters at the foot of the building
are worthy of special attention.

192. Glacier des Bois
Pencil and water-colour

A very attractive example showing Ruskin's power to
reproduce the essential features of a landscape. The
colouring is very delicate and the whole impression one
of great loveliness.

193. Alpine study
Sepia and Chinese white

A vivid, austere Alpine study with rushing waters in
the foreground. Snow-capped peaks are outlined in the
distance. Great precipitous rocks rise out of the waters.

194. Chamoix Lenes
Aiguille Charmoz, from window
Water-colour and pencil

A brilliant, hasty mountain drawing. Seen from a little
distance, the masses of rocks emerging from snow are very
real. In order to appreciate the delicacy of even a hasty
drawing like this, the tiny houses and cluster of trees on
the right-hand side of the picture towards the top should
be seen. Similarly, a little house in the centre of the
picture should be noticed. Look, too, at the mountain
stream which, beginning up in the mountains, is seen
towards the right-hand side of the picture and comes
almost to the foot.

195. Valley of Hasli, from above Maringen

Ink

A delightful drawing. In the foreground there is a ruined tower, with a curved window. In the centre in the foreground is the valley. A little village with its church is drawn in the centre of the valley.

196. Wellhorn and Glacier de Rosenlaui, from Rosenlaui

Ink

The mountains are the chief feature in the picture, and the valley between the glacier is shown. There is a distant view of more mountains, and in the foreground there is a fine study of trees, with a road on the left of the drawing.

197. Stone carving at Venice

Pencil

Inscribed 'Make lines of fracture firm and beautiful and head entirely dark on this light, but hold stone dark on the marble ground'

The drawing is of a piece of sculpture at the head of a column between arches. The sculptured figure shows a man in a long cloak with sword and shield.

198. St. George, from Carpaccio

Pencil

Inscribed 'J R Giorgio de Schiavoni June 1812'

This drawing is a detail taken from Carpaccio's drawing of St. George killing the dragon, at Venice. It is interesting to observe how this drawing conveys the life-like attitude of the horse and rider.

199. Building with Tower

Pencil

A very hasty sketch done, apparently, in Italy.

200. St. Mark's, Venice

Pencil and ink.   December 1884

An interesting drawing showing the side of St. Mark's, with the view of two sides of the Piazza. The drawing belongs to Ruskin's later period, but shows his powers undiminished. The drawing is interesting because of the great number of human figures introduced. This was unusual with him.

201. Bridge

Pencil and wash

This may be the beginning of a drawing of the Ponte Vecchio at Florence. Seen at a little distance, the water flowing under the bridge is seen to great advantage. The distant view through the arch on the left is cleverly indicated.

202. Church at Châlons sur Marne

Pencil

Inscribed 'J. Ruskin, 1835'

This is one of Ruskin's early drawings, done at the age of 16, showing the church with its flying buttresses, with houses on the left of the picture. Note the charming details with which Ruskin gives the pinnacles at the top of the tower.

203. Study of dead bird

Water-colour

This was done in fifteen minutes by Ruskin at the Working Men's College, Ormond Street.

204. Bienne

Inscribed 'Great Square, Bienne'

Another of Ruskin's early sketches. All these early sketches show the same delightful characteristics—sympathy, power of rendering detail, accuracy of hand and eye.

205. Berne

Inscribed 'Street scene Berne. J. Ruskin 1835 signed 1880'

This drawing shows a most glorious window on the left of the picture.

206. Verona: View of River with Bridge

Pencil

The effect of this very interesting drawing gives it the atmosphere of a delicate etching, especially in the treatment of the trees.

207. Sculptured heads at Amiens Cathedral

Pencil

This drawing should be examined in connexion with No. 178 dealing with the same subject.

208. Mountain and Lake scene

Water-colour

The mountain rises from the waters of the lake. It is an impressive drawing showing the forces of nature at work on the mountain-side.

209. Study of Arch, Venice

Water-colour

The marble stone and the carving along the edge of the arch are well suggested.

210. ## Studies of Rocks

Ink, pencil, and wash

Four sketches, inscribed at foot of mount 'Relations of form in alternating hard and soft rocks'.

Underneath the various drawings are the following inscriptions by Ruskin:

Under the first sketch: 'Mont Blanc from Geneva seen over back of Salève'.

'Charmioz Torasses Géant Midi Blaitière.'

Under the second sketch: 'Gault and Rudisten-kalk in the Dorons above Sallanches.'

Under the third sketch: 'Gault in the ranges between Bonneville and Annecy. The cone A is a power bed. I believe the cone A and continuation BB are the bed of base of Reposoir. Above the Brezon CCC all higher.'

Under the fourth sketch: 'Outline from Geneva. Built 4 c. See coloured sketch. Relation of Town in alternating hard and soft rocks.'

211. ## St. Gotthard

Pencil

Inscribed 'St. Gotthard Pass from near Fluelen'

A hasty sketch showing the road between the mountains.

212. ## St. Gotthard

Ink

Inscribed 'Study for etching of Turner's St. Gotthard in 4th vol. of M.P.'

A very delicate mountain drawing.

213. ## Abingdon

Pencil

Inscribed 'Abingdon 1872. Sketch for composition signed 1879 J. R.'

On the right-hand side is a country road bordered with

trees, with a distant spire. On the left of the picture the eyes are carried across fields to a distant landscape with a church in the centre.

214. Drawing of Gothic window, Venice
Pencil

The top portion of the window is shown in a realistic drawing.

215. Central Boss from the Frari Church
Ink, water-colour, and wash

Inscribed 'The leaves of the crockets have all full ribs and turned lobes. Central boss of the stalls of the Frari. Note the leaf-shaped penetrations, and the ridge rib of the tracery'

An exquisite detail, exquisitely drawn.

216. An arch over a window
Water-colour

Inscribed 'Windows of coloured marble. This had I doubt not tracery'

The arch and its essential details are carefully shown. On the left Ruskin has drawn capitals at the top of the supporting pillars immediately underneath the arch.

217. An arch
Water-colour, ink, and pencil

Inscribed 'I believe middle arch of the palace I restored'

The inscription was evidently written at a much later date after the drawing had been made.

It is a clear, simple drawing. On the left-hand side there is a characteristic insertion of detail.

218. Capital

Water-colour and ink

Inscribed 'Capital supporting canopy of the tomb with St. Joseph in Frari. (Arnaldos?) No. 1 in arranged sheet'

A most attractive and vivid little drawing.

219. Vesuvius

Water-colour

A drawing of Vesuvius in eruption. This was done by Ruskin during a visit to Italy in 1840.

The style has been thought to be a little unlike Ruskin's, and he himself thought so too, but in later years was emphatic that it was typical of the kind of work he did in 1840. It is a vivid drawing. The treatment of the distant view gives Turner-like effects and shows the influence of that master.

220. Piazza S. Maria del Pianto

Pencil and tint

This is a reproduction of the original drawing which was one of those presented by the author of this book to the Italian nation in 1932.

This sketch was made by Ruskin on December 3rd, 1841. He had noted the subject a day or two previously, and the following entry in his diary on December 1st, 1841, refers to this picture:

'Found throughout a long walk not one subject which, if sketched carelessly or in a hurry, would have been fit for anything; and not a single corner of a street which, if studied closely and well, would not be beautiful. So completely is this place picturesque, down to its door-knockers, and so entirely does that picturesqueness depend not on any important lines or real beauty of object, but upon the little bits of contrasted feeling—the old clothes hanging out of a marble architrave—that architrave smashed at one side and built into a piece of Roman frieze, which moulders away the next instant into a patch of broken brickwork—projecting over a mouldering wooden window, supported in its turn on a bit of grey entablature with a vestige of inscription; but all to be studied closely, before it can be felt or even seen, and, I am persuaded, quite lost to the eyes of all but a few artists.'

221. Wall veil decoration, Venice

Water-colour

This is the original drawing for the plate which appears in *The Stones of Venice*, vol. 1, No. 13.

On the left-hand side is Renaissance work, on the other side Romanesque, from S. Petro of Pistoja. The work on the left is from the Arthur Club House, St. James's Street.

For a description of the points raised in this drawing *The Stones of Venice* should be consulted, pages 348 onwards, in vol. 1 of the Library edition.

222. Chamouni, the Glacier des Bois

Water-colour

A vivid and detailed drawing. This sketch is specially interesting. Ruskin writes in 1874 from Chamouni to Charles Eliot Norton:

'The Glacier des Bois is no more. Of that of our days is left a little white tongue of ice showing in the blank bed. . . . But the saddest of all is Mont Blanc itself from here—it is, to what it was, as a mere whitewashed wall to a bridecake. When the snow is level nearly, it holds on pretty well, but on the steep Bionnassay valley it has all flowed down and consumed away.'

In a later letter written in the same year to Mrs. John

Simon he says: 'By the way, have you the quick, slight sketch in colour of the Bouchard and Glacier des Bois, now valuable as a record?'

223. Sierre

Pencil

Inscribed 'Sierre looks a lovely subject, but too much dead wall in shape, needs figures also else I would have gone back to draw it'

Ruskin's description of this as a lovely subject is well deserved. The towers and chimneys of the building in the middle of the picture are extremely picturesque, and the whole composition is most attractive.

224. Gothic ornament

Ink and wash

There are five separate drawings on this sheet, which were done for *The Stones of Venice*, and show the contrast between severe and florid gothic ornament.

225. Verona

Pencil

Inscribed 'Verona 30th Oct. 76'

The main interest of this pencil sketch at Verona is the central gateway through which an attractive vista is seen.

226. Watersmeet of Greta and Tees

Pencil. 1876

Inscribed on drawing 'Greta and Tees'. Inscribed on mount 'Junction of. Signed March 17 1889. Sketch on spot. With Arthur and Joan on last posting expedition from London to Brantwood. I may retouch with colour some day yet (17 May 1889) but write more for information down streams Greta–Tees'

The drawing reflects Ruskin's inquiring and scientific

mind. He was always interested in rivers, their history, and their influence.

227. Montreuil

Pencil

Inscribed on drawing 'Montreuil 26th Aug 1882'. Inscribed on mount 'Note old well. Driven to from Avallon'

The old well referred to in Ruskin's inscription on the mount is on the left side of the drawing. In the centre of the drawing there is a winding road with buildings on each side.

228. Avallon

Pencil. 1882

The drawing shows a winding road flanked by mountains on one side with lovely clouds and trees to the left of the road.

In this hasty sketch the right-hand bottom corner is done with curious detail.

229. Kempten

Ink

Inscribed underneath drawing 'Kempten C. Church steeple in Kempten B. D. on other side.' Inscribed on right-hand side of drawing 'Black thing? What? Wish I knew! 1873'

A hasty pencil drawing of a church steeple but with the charm of all these Kempten drawings.

229a. Drawings at Kempten

Ink and pencil

Inscribed on left 'Kempten D. Tower and bit below in Kempten B.' On right 'Bridge in Kempten A.'

These drawings are on the back of No. 229. They consist of tower (top left), a bridge (top right), and houses and other buildings (bottom left).

230. Drawing of Tower, Kempten

Pencil

Inscribed 'Kempten E. Tower in Kempten B. Getting up towards it. See back'

A very delightful pencil drawing of the tower which is also shown in 229*a*.

230*a*. Kempten

Ink and pencil

Inscribed 'Kempten 1859. Another on back. Kempten F. View from foot of tower. Got up to see after dinner walk'

A most interesting sketch—hasty, but with many details and long views.

231. Fiesole

Pencil

Inscribed 'San Dominico Fiesole 25th Aug. 74'

A walled road is shown in this drawing with the church on the right-hand side.

232. Arch masonry

Ink

This drawing contains eight separate divisions, each giving illustrations of arches. It is reproduced in the Library edition of Ruskin's works, vol. ix, facing page 168. Sixteen separate arches are shown. The drawing is one of very great delicacy and beauty, particularly the sections numbered on the drawing 5 and 6, but indeed the remark applies to all of them.

The sections are numbered 1 to 8. No. 1 is from St. Antonio, Padua. No. 2 is from the Cathedral of Sens. No. 3 is a window from Carnarvon Castle. No. 4 is from a little belfry in a Swiss village above Vevey. No. 5 is from

San Fermo of Verona. No. 6 is from the Eremitani,
Padua. No. 7 is from the Frari, Venice. No. 8 illustrates
the construction of arches with three and five pieces. A
full description of these arches is given in the volume of
the Library edition already quoted.

The drawing is signed by Ruskin, and also by T. S.
Boys, the engraver.

233. Peacocks and Crosses. Sketch for *The Stones of Venice*

Ink, pencil, and wash

This sheet contains six separate drawings, three of crosses
and three of peacocks. They are reproduced in vol. x of
the Library edition, facing page 166, and bear the title of
'Byzantine Sculpture'.

A full description of these pieces of sculpture is given
in the same volume of the Library edition on page 166.
Ruskin did few drawings more exquisite in detail than
these. They repay the closest attention.

234. Bases of pillars for *The Stones of Venice*

Ink and water-colour

This is another example of the drawings Ruskin did for
The Stones of Venice. There are twelve separate drawings
on this sheet. It is reproduced in vol. ix of the Library
edition, page 342.

The drawings illustrate the decoration at the bases of
columns, taken from various buildings.

A full description of this plate is given by Ruskin on
pages 342 and 343 in the volume quoted.

Even to any one without any knowledge or great
interest in architecture, these drawings reveal unexpected
features of interest, and are a great help to the study of
buildings.

235. Schaffhausen

Pencil

Inscribed 'Schaffhausen Steep bank of broken earth and rock'

A general view of Schaffhausen, in which the town is seen in relation to the surrounding hills. Although a slight pencil sketch, it conveys the beauty of the landscape.

236. Leaves and berries. Two drawings

Water-colour

Inscribed under the first drawing 'Exercise first wash leaving lights. Second filling. J. Ruskin Brantwood. Jan 1873'

Inscribed under the second drawing 'Exercise keep your red red and your brown brown and your green green for your life. J. Ruskin Brantwood Jan 1873'

These two drawings were done by Ruskin as a definite lesson in water-colour. The one on the left is a bunch of small branches with leaves. On the right is a drawing showing berries and green leaves.

237. Landscape outline

Ink and pencil

An extraordinarily interesting drawing showing on the left side of the picture a straggling town, and delightful sketches of houses, and in the background ranges of mountains. The right of the picture is in pencil, and less finished than the remainder.

238. Mosaics. Drawn for *The Stones of Venice*

These drawings of characteristic delicacy are reproduced in vol. xi of the Library edition, facing page 211. They are mosaics of an olive tree and flowers.

They are fully described in the volume mentioned, beginning on page 211.

P

239. Florence

Pencil

Inscribed 'Florence western sky I believe seen over Ponte di Trinita, but puzzles me at last'

This is a hasty drawing of the Trinità bridge at Florence. There is a boat under the central arch of the bridge. Looking through this central arch, a second bridge is seen.

240. Alps from Munich

Ink and wash

Inscribed 'Field of corn, Munich. A joins B look for A. Munich Alps and Tyrol. Saturday July 23 1859'

The drawing is an outline of the Alps as seen from Munich. They have a map-like precision.

241. Sketches in British Museum of birds, &c.

Pencil

Inscribed 'Notes in Brit Mus J. R. 1872'

Under three of the drawings Ruskin has written Shoveller, Mallard, and Eagle respectively.

There is an interesting drawing of a human face.

242. Moulding at Chartres Cathedral

Pencil and wash

This careful drawing gives six details of the drawing, the one at the foot of the drawing is apparently the head of a saint.

243. Edge decoration. Drawn for *The Stones of Venice*

This sheet contains a large number of drawings. The plate is reproduced in *The Stones of Venice*, Library edition, vol. IX, facing page 318.

The drawing of an arch and canopy, No. 7, is a fine example. Ruskin gives a description of the plate, beginning on page 318 of the volume mentioned above.

244. Mouldings, drawn for *The Stones of Venice*
Wash and ink

These are reproduced in *The Stones of Venice*, vol. IX of the Library edition, page 365.

245. Bonneville
Pencil

Inscribed 'Golden sunshine near Bonneville Savoy J. R. 1862'
The drawing shows a mass of trees on the right-hand side with remarkable buildings on the left.

246. Ravine at Maglans, Valley of Cluses
Water-colour

A detailed study of great rocks. The trees help us to understand the magnitude of the ravine.

247. Buildings at Verona
Pencil

A very good example of Ruskin's architectural work. He loved high groups of houses. All of his sketches on these subjects live in the naturalness that he gives them.

248. Abbeville
Water-colour

This is a superb example of Ruskin's water-colour work. The cathedral is rendered with extreme delicacy, but part of the attractiveness is due to the bridge on the right-hand side of the picture and the houses over and on either side of the bridge. It is a splendid example of architectural drawing which is so much more. It is a most satisfying picture full of beauty and restfulness.

249. Rome : Trevi Fountain
Water-colour and wash

A very attractive drawing of the most famous fountain in

Rome. It is not finished in detail, but it well gives the attractiveness of the fountain.

250. Castelbarco Tomb, Verona

Pencil

Inscribed 'St. Anastasia, Verona'

Ruskin did a large water-colour drawing of this tomb (see No. 65). It is interesting to compare the two. This is a very careful architectural drawing. It is an exact and faithful piece of work and it has the charm which all sympathetic work possesses. There was always a singular grace in Ruskin's pencil.

251. Lake of Brienz

Water-colour

This is an important water-colour drawing as it shows the resourcefulness of Ruskin. On the left is a hill covered with trees and flowers. In the background are mountain ranges. There is an effective treatment of clouds, in the mountains, on the right-hand side of the picture. One of the glories of this little drawing is the way in which Ruskin shows the colours of the mountains and sky reflected in the waters of the lake.

252. Tyrolese mountains

Ink and pencil

Inscribed 'A Tyrolese mountains from Munich. Joins B. J.R. 1859. B Tyrolese mountains from Munich joins A. J.R. 1859'

The drawing is in two parts, one part being lettered A, and the other part being lettered B.

This is one of many drawings which Ruskin made to record accurately the physical features of a district about which he was afterwards going to write, and especially the relation of physical features to nearby towns and cities.

253. Bridge at Terni

Water-colour. 1840

A very attractive water-colour. The centre of the drawing is occupied by the bridge, and the precipitous nature of the scenery is suggested by the view through the bridge. On the bridge itself are very ornamental buildings. On the left of the bridge are houses. On the right other buildings are shown. In the background the mountains are impressively shown. It is an admirable drawing full of life and interest.

254. Egyptian figure

Outlined in brown crayon and white

A drawing of an Egyptian figure showing a woman holding a Lotus flower.

There is a further coloured diagram on the picture. It is signed J. Ruskin.

255. Lucca: Tower of the Guinigi Palace

Water-colour. 1845

Reproduced in *Praeterita*, vol. xxxv, page 347, of the Library edition.

A very wonderful drawing full of beauty. The tower of the Palace is only one feature of great interest in the composition. The colonnade in the foreground, and on the right, with trees and masses of creepers, give an atmosphere of great charm.

256. Ramparts of Sens

Wash and pencil. 1846

Inscribed 'Ramparts of Sens, Sens April 15 J. Ruskin 1846
Signed 1879'

An interesting study of trees in which Ruskin has concentrated upon the strength of their trunks.

257. A tree study

Water-colour and pencil

Another example of Ruskin's study of trees. In the centre of the picture there is a stone archway and wall. In front and all around are studies of trees.

258. Naples

Water-colour. 1841

Inscribed 'Naples'

A very delightful study of houses in Naples. The upper part of the picture is specially interesting, but the whole makes a wonderful composition.

Special features of it are the care which Ruskin has shown in drawing the windows, and other architectural features. Some of them are ruins, and an extremely realistic impression is obtained.

259. Hôtel de Ville, Louvain

Pencil and wash

Inscribed 'Hotel de Ville, Louvain Mine after Prout J. R.'

This is a drawing in pencil and wash done by Ruskin at an early age, when he was greatly under the influence of Prout. The mannerisms of his master are reproduced. The whole picture is of extraordinary interest as showing the infinite power which Ruskin had for copying details.

The four windows in the Hôtel immediately below the roof should be particularly noted. The arches and other features are given with great fidelity. On the right of the picture there is a bit of an interesting building, apparently a church with gargoyles above. The drawing is noteworthy for the many figures introduced at the foot. Ruskin did not introduce many figures into his drawings.

260. Study of rocks and torrent
Water-colour

A very lively drawing in which the action of the water upon the rocks is well given. The colour of the rock in the left-hand corner and the leaves around it are shown in some detail.

261. Simrishamn
Pencil

Inscribed 'Ingegeral Simrishamn'

An architectural study showing the top of several arches, with carved figures above.

262. Sketches of two crocodiles
Pencil and wash

Ruskin made many drawings of animals and birds, most of them life-like and natural, but with an element of humour.

263. Street Scene
Pencil

This is an attractive pencil drawing of a street with houses on each side leading to an outlet under a building which is built across the road. I have not been able to trace the locality.

264. Renaissance and Romanesque masonry contrasted
Ink and wash

This is one of many drawings made by Ruskin for *The Stones of Venice*, in which work it was reproduced.

265. Buildings at Lucca
Pencil. 1882

Inscribed 'Lucca J. R. 1882'

A rapid pencil drawing.

266. Sketch on the Ponte Vecchio

Pencil.   1882

A rough pencil drawing.

267. Castle on Hill

Ink

Inscribed 'After J. M. W. T. J. Ruskin 1874'

Ruskin was fond of copying Turner. This is one of many similar examples.

268. San Miniato, Florence

Water-colour

A very beautiful drawing of a part of the façade. On the right-hand side at the foot is a vivid reproduction of part of a picture in colour. The decoration at the top is finely done, so too are the squared panels underneath.

269. Malham Cove

Water-colour

Inscribed 'Malham Cove'

A delicate piece of drawing showing high cliffs.

270. Building near river

Pencil

A hasty pencil sketch of buildings apparently on the side of a river. There is a distant bridge suggested on the right of the drawing.

271. Study of Capitals

Pencil

A very delicate and sympathetic work of great attractiveness done for *The Stones of Venice*, showing the capitals of two columns and part of arches above.

272. Bienne

Pencil

Inscribed 'Bienne A steps down Horrid puzzle'

The drawing shows a part of the town with steeples and towers.

273. Spur at base of pillar, Venice

Water-colour

Two stone figures and masonry.

274. Spur at base of pillar, Venice

Water-colour

This and the preceding drawing are details of the base of a pillar on the west side of the Piazzetta. This drawing shows two figures with net and fishes.

275. Venice

Water-colour

A drawing showing the entrance to the Grand Canal. On the left is the church of the Salute. In the centre is the Doges' Palace. An evening effect with interesting cloud studies.

276. Bell tower and capital

Pencil

A small sketch showing bell under canopy erected on another tower, which may be a shrine. Detail of a capital at the side.

277. Arches at Venice

Pencil

Very small sketches of details of Venetian arches. It is interesting to see the minute coat of arms carved in stone over the doorway at the foot of the drawing.

Q

278. Balcony and windows at Venice

Pencil

A delightful and characteristic sketch of typical Gothic windows and balustrade.

279. Gothic capital at Venice

Ink and wash

Two drawings, one showing the capital the other the forms of leaves composing the capital.

280. A Wild Drake

Water-colour

This rapid drawing conveys both the life and the beauty of the bird.

281. Water, Hills, and Cloud Study

Water-colour

An extremely beautiful drawing. In the foreground is water, its shore a beautifully drawn hill. Above the hill are clouds with mountain-tops emerging. On the right is a building with a small tower.

282. Troutbeck, Westmorland

Pencil

Inscribed 'In Troutbeck, Westmorland, August 7th 1837. J. Ruskin. Signed 7th Jan 1880'

The two dates in the inscription are explained by the fact that Ruskin frequently signed his drawings in old age, giving the date when he signed them as well as the date when he made the drawings. He was about $18\frac{1}{2}$ when this lakeland sketch was made showing a rather large farm-house with a curious round chimney. In the foreground are rocks and water.

283. Ben Venue and Trossachs over Achray

Pencil

Inscribed 'Ben Venue and Trossachs over Achray July 25th '38. J. Ruskin. Signed December 28th 1879'

This is another early drawing by Ruskin. It shows lake, mountains, and rocks. It is a delightful composition full of spirit.

284. Château Lausanne, Sunrise

Water-colour. 1845

The château is shown amidst its glorious surroundings. A great valley to the right, a range of mountains showing blue through the clouds in the background. The drawing is strongly reminiscent of Turner and might indeed be mistaken for one of his works. The cloud effect at the top of the drawing on the left is well done.

285. Château Lausanne, Moonrise

Water-colour. 1845

This drawing is of the same scene as described above, but giving the effect of moonrise instead of sunrise. There is some difference in the aspect of the château from which the drawings are made. The main features, however, are common to both drawings. In this one, the mountains stand out with more emphasis. The mistiness of sunrise has disappeared.

286. Houses at Naples

Pencil and water-colour

In connexion with this drawing the following extract from Ruskin's works is of interest and importance:

' . . . In the winter of 1840 and spring of 1841 I was at Rome, Naples and Venice making a series of pencil sketches partly in imitation of Prout, partly of David

Roberts. I had not the smallest notion of writing about art at that time (many people, myself included, thought I was dying and should never write about anything). These sketches, though full of weaknesses and vulgarities, have also much good in them: two are placed at Oxford as records of Venice, of which one was used to paint from by Prout himself, and all of them are of historical interest in their accuracy of representation.'

The drawing is most successful in giving so naturally the mass effect of the buildings shown.

287. Water scene with trees

Pencil and wash

A group of trees is shown on the right of the picture with little foliage, stark and lonely. Hilly tongues of land are shown jutting out into the water, forming lagoon-like channels. In the right foreground steps and a seat are suggested.

288. Salerno

Pencil and wash. 1841

An impressive drawing giving an atmosphere of much dignity to a very interesting building. In the foreground is a fountain. The way in which Ruskin draws such details as the windows gives distinction to the whole. The occasional tiny touches in white are very effective.

289. Ironwork, Sion, Valais

Ink

Inscribed 'Ironwork, Sion, Valais'

'At 1, 2, 3, the points seem to vanish in air.' This remark refers to three numbers which Ruskin has inserted in the pattern. He was always greatly interested in the craft of ironwork and this is a good example of many careful

drawings which he made. The beautiful flower-like effect
on the right-hand side of the drawing should be studied.
The iron bracket is intended to hold a lamp. The chains
for the lamp are indicated over Ruskin's words 'Chains
to lamp'.

290. Capital
Water-colour

This is a Renaissance capital which Ruskin describes as
a good type of capital in a fine time.

291. The Avocet
Pencil

Inscribed 'Young Avocet real size'

A most vivid and life-like drawing. It is reproduced in
vol. xxv of the Library edition. A copy of the engraving
by Hugh Allen is shown in the same frame.

292. Sea and Cliffs
Water-colour

The sea is very successfully treated and a realistic effect
is given where the shallow water has reached the sand and
reflects the buildings above. Over the uncovered sand
Ruskin has written 'Drab sand'.

293. Hill, water, and meadows
Water-colour

This drawing is taken from one of Ruskin's sketch-books.
In the foreground cattle are grazing. Beyond the river
there is a pleasant hill. An interesting, disturbed sky is
shown.

294. Road to Florence
Water-colour. 1845

An important drawing. The sunny road is seen on the

extreme left, with heavy shadows from the trees which
border it. The greater part of the drawing shows a great
wooded bank. The trees are drawn with great fidelity and
if the details are closely studied it will be seen that extraordinary care has been taken in drawing them. The
drawing of foliage of the trees is strongly reminiscent of
the drawings which Ruskin did when a young boy.

295. Pompeii
Water-colour

In the foreground there rises a stark building at the foot
of the slopes of the mountain. The latter is very carefully
drawn and will repay careful study.

296. Scala Monument, Verona
Wash and pencil

Two sketches of figures in this famous monument. The
delicate carving at the base of the figures is suggested.

297. Pont Remy
Water-colour

Inscribed 'Pont Remy'

This is not a very clear composition. It is apparently an
autumn scene. There are distant views of hills and clouds.

298. Landscape
Water-colour

A view of hills and sky. The clouds in the light of the
setting sun are very attractive.

299. Tilberthwaite Glen
Water-colour

A most delicate and sympathetic drawing. It gives a view
of the glen from the main waterfall. The trees on the

rocks are drawn with exquisite care. So, too, are the rocks. The drawing was probably done in the early spring, before the prevailing brown colour has given way before the growth of spring.

300. South Gate, Winchelsea
Water-colour
Inscribed 'Hakewitt, South Gate, Winchelsea'

A very sympathetic drawing, the main feature of which is the entrance in ruins covered with foliage. There is a distant view of trees through the gateway.

301. Detail from Michelangelo
Ink

An outline drawing of one of Michelangelo's figures on the ceiling of the Sistine Chapel. Ruskin made an enormous number of copies of details from many Italian and other painters for use in his lectures and writings.

302. Detail from Raphael
Ink

An outline drawing from Raphael's Madonna with the Infant Christ and St. John.

303. Detail of Capital
Pencil and wash

A drawing of a Venetian Renaissance capital.

304. From the Col de la Seigne
Water-colour and pencil

This drawing is reproduced in vol. xxvi of the Library edition. It is unfinished but is a vivid piece of work.

305. Pompeii

Pencil and wash

A realistic drawing showing ruins standing stark against a background of mountains.

306. Bonneville

Water-colour.   1862

This is a view from the base of the Brezon before Bonneville, looking towards Geneva. The Juras in the distance, Salene on the left. This drawing is reproduced in vol. XVII of the Library edition. It was formerly in the possession of W. Pritchard Gordon. It is a remarkable drawing, covering a large area of country containing a great deal of detail. The whole is a thing of great beauty.

307. Lucerne

Water-colour

A wonderful drawing of the walls of Lucerne. The splash of colour upon the buildings is given with extraordinary effectiveness. The details of this drawing deserve the most careful study. Look, for instance, at the plants growing on the sunlit wall to the right of the main tower. They could not be more exquisitely drawn. From the collection of W. Pritchard Gordon.

308. Cutter Inn, Ely

Pencil and ink

This drawing is inscribed 'Cutter Inn Ely Sept 1877'

It shows the inn with trees around it and with the river in the foreground.

309. Sunset

Water-colour

The drawing shows a village amid hills, the sun setting behind the most distant hill amid a blaze of glory.

310. Mountains, clouds, and water

Water-colour

From the water in the foreground the mountains rise into a mass of stormy clouds. There is a sailing-boat towards the right of the picture.

311. Three Towers

Water-colour

The three towers, which are very delicately drawn, rise amid a background of mountains. On the right is a glimpse of water.

312. Avallon

Pencil

Inscribed 'Avallon 21st August '82 J. R.'

A rapid pencil sketch showing buildings on a hill. In the foreground, on the left, is a path by a wall.

313. Canterbury

Pencil

Inscribed 'J. Ruskin Canterbury 1832, my first as ever was study of architecture. Signed 15th Jan 1880'

A drawing done when Ruskin was 13, of great biographical interest.

314. Canterbury

Pencil. 1832

Inscribed 'J. Ruskin Canterbury South Porch 1832. Signed 15th Jan 1880'

This drawing was executed at the same time as the one above and both show the same extraordinary power of exact drawing of detail which marked all Ruskin's work.

R

315. Study of a leaf
Water-colour

An attractive drawing showing the structure and colour of the leaf.

316. Study of four leaves
Water-colour and pencil
Inscribed 'John Ruskin 9th Oct '89'

Three of the leaves on this sprig are in pencil, the other in water-colour. The structure of the leaves is vividly expressed.

317. Italian town
Ink and wash

A very attractive drawing of an Italian town. There are typical towers rising out of a pleasing mass of buildings. The town is in the midst of hills.

318. Venetian capitals
Pencil, ink, and wash

Nine drawings of Venetian capitals. They are reproduced in *The Stones of Venice*.

No more striking example could be shown of Ruskin's power of rendering minute details in a way which compels the admiration of every one. No better drawings of their kind have ever been done. The bottom drawing on the left-hand side should be especially studied, and so should each and all of them.

319. Amiens
Pencil on grey paper touched with white
Inscribed 'John Ruskin Amiens 1881'

A view showing the river bank with buildings and trees in the background.

320. Lucerne

Water-colour

An attractive drawing of the town showing the famous bridge and mountains in the background. On the back of this drawing is another giving a more general view of Lucerne, the lake, and mountains.

321. Boulogne Harbour

Ink

Inscribed 'A collier on shore "The Gazelle off Boulogne Harbour 1861"'

A vivid drawing of the ship being unloaded on the shore. The sailors are busy in the rigging.

322. Kingfisher's foot

Water-colour

Inscribed 'Kingfisher's foot (dried) J. R. 1871'

Three very delicate drawings showing with great care the structure of the foot from different angles.

323. Tomb of Doge Francesco Dandolo

Water-colour

A drawing of two small trees at the head and foot of the Madonna's couch on the tomb of the Doge Francesco Dandolo at Venice. There is a description of this tomb in *The Stones of Venice*, chapter 2, page 91 of the Library edition, vol. xi.

324. Grand Canal, Venice

Pencil

A drawing of a part of the Grand Canal. The palace on the right stands out more boldly than the rest of the buildings. The palaces on the other side of the canal contain much delicate pencil-work. This sketch was probably done by Ruskin during the winter of 1875–6 which he spent at Venice. During this visit to Venice Ruskin enjoyed the society of Professor Moore of Harvard University who had been introduced to him by Professor Norton. Professor Moore was his frequent companion in Venice, where they sketched and studied together.

325. Church among hills
Water-colour

An old building with a belfry, standing amidst hills.

326. Market-place in Italian town
Ink, pencil, and wash

A scene of simple interest and beauty of a kind which always appealed to Ruskin. A sketch full of life and interest.

327. Detail from the Tomb of Can Signorio della Scala, Verona
Water-colour

This is one of the statues from the famous tomb of Can Signorio della Scala, of which a fuller drawing is shown in No. 88 in this collection. The two should be studied in conjunction.

328. Detail from the Tomb of Can Grande della Scala, Verona
Pencil, heightened with white

This is an interesting pencil drawing of the sculptured figure of Can Grande, the head of the Scala family, which appears on his tomb, erected about the year 1335. Ruskin thus describes this tomb in *The Stones of Venice*, in a general description of the great gothic tombs:

'At Verona . . . so early as about the year 1335, the con-

summate form of the Gothic tomb occurs in the monument of Can Grande della Scala. It is set over the portal
of the chapel anciently belonging to the family. The sarcophagus is sculptured with shallow bas-reliefs, representing
(which is rare in the tombs with which I am acquainted in
Italy, unless they are those of the saints) the principal
achievements of the warrior's life, especially the siege of
Vicenza and battle of Placenza; these sculptures, however,
form little more than a chased and roughened groundwork
for the fully relieved statues representing the Annunciation, projecting boldly from the front of the sarcophagus.
Above, the Lord of Verona is laid in his long robe of civil
dignity, wearing the simple bonnet, consisting merely of
a fillet bound round the brow, knotted and falling on the
shoulder. He is laid as asleep; his arms crossed upon his
body, and his sword by his side. Above him, a bold arched
canopy is sustained by two projecting shafts, and on the
pinnacle of its roof is the statue of the knight on his war-
horse; his helmet, dragon-winged and crested with the
dog's head, tossed back behind his shoulders, and the
broad and blazoned drapery floating back from his horse's
breast—so truly drawn by the old workman from the life,
that it seems to wave in the wind, and the knight's spear
to shake, and his marble horse to be evermore quickening
its pace, and starting into heavier and hastier charge, as
the silver clouds float past behind it in the sky.'

329. Bas-relief from the tomb of Can Grande della Scala, Verona

Pencil

This is a drawing of one of the bas-reliefs on the sarcophagus of the monument to Can Grande della Scala at
Verona. They represent the principal achievements of the
warrior's life. The monument was erected about 1335.

330. Detail of the tomb of Can Grande della Scala, Verona

Water-colour

This is a drawing of one of the statues representing the Annunciation which projects from the front of the sarcophagus. It is, of course, the figure of the Virgin. The student will naturally refer to Ruskin's whole treatment of this and other of the great Gothic tombs in the passage from which the note to No. 328 in this collection is taken.

331. Tree Study at Vevey

Pencil and water-colour

Inscribed 'Hills above Vevay 10th August'

Ruskin makes this simple study—mainly of a tree trunk —a thing of beauty.

332. The Great St. Bernard

Water-colour

A study of the famous monastery in its romantic surroundings.

333. Study of roofs and balconies

Ink, pencil, and wash, heightened with white

Inscribed '(1845) Between Lecco and Bergamo. J. R. to Alex. D.D. Wedderburn 1877'

A very characteristic drawing with details most attractively rendered.

334. Study of an Iris

Water-colour

The drawing shows a rich sense of colour.

335. Botanical studies

Ink, wash, and water-colour

Inscribed 'Rays unexpanded Green calyx outside and successive descending basts, real size, termination of ray. It has always 13 leaves (rays) arranged if I mistake not slightly pentagon fashion a. essential form b. showing section. 5. Senecio Jacobaea F.6.944. Common ragwort. Conf. for graceful calyx F.D.1652.'

A good example of his scientific accuracy.

336. Botanical studies

Ink and pencil

The drawings are lifelike and bring out a sense of design, balance, and natural grouping.

337. Botanical study

Water-colour

Inscribed 'Les Rousses. Breakfast-time 4th Sept 82 J. R. See page 34 diary'

Another example of his careful nature studies in his later life.

338. Botanical studies

Water-colour

Inscribed 'Portuguese narcissus Brantwood 1878. 2. p. 114 Egypt II'

Further careful flower studies.

339. Botanical studies

Water-colour

The originals are exquisitely coloured. Ruskin's flower studies were most important and his writings on the subject are authoritative.

340. Botanical studies

Ink and wash

Inscribed 'Silver-weed. Back of flower pulled off stalk showing calyx. Yellow corolla, concave-petaled below

convex on upper surface. Bud-profile. Bud—from above.
Something wrong. This must be a potentilla—4 not 5
Perfect type of sedum flowers Black spot.'

These drawings, of which he did hundreds, reveal Ruskin's serious study of botany.

341. Hôtel de Ville, Brussels

Pencil

This is a copy by Ruskin from Prout's Sketches in
Flanders and Germany. It is greatly reduced in size and
is a remarkable piece of work.

342. Study of cottages

Pencil

Inscribed 'Rich confusion of lower cottages'

A very delightful drawing with most attractive details
given with Ruskin's usual skill. The balustrade and parts
of the roofs are examples.

343. Study of a piece of Rock with Quartz veining

Water-colour

A characteristic rock drawing done with great care and
realism.

344. A Page from Ruskin's First Sketch-book

Pencil

It is significant that Ruskin's first sketch-book was used
mainly for architectural and tree studies.

345. Another page from Ruskin's First Sketch-book

Pencil

These drawings show the spirit of fidelity which later was
so marked.

Epilogue

Epilogue: Some Personal Notes

I SHOULD be sorry for this book to end without some reference on my part to young friends who have helped with the great collection of Ruskin's works at Bembridge. There has always been a boy curator of the Galleries since they were opened in the year 1930, and all who have held the post have given me valuable help with the catalogue which has occupied my spare moments for some years. I express my gratitude to all of them—Colin, Ian, Donald, Neville, Leslie, Alec, and Peter.

But there are two ex-curators to whose work I must pay a special tribute. Colin Rocke was the first curator of the collection and gave strenuous service in connexion with the original arrangement of the galleries and their cataloguing. Donald Sutcliffe gave unfailing help with the catalogue and in connexion with the care of individual drawings. Both of these young students showed high qualities of taste and criticism, and spent much time in the mounting, cleaning, and hanging of many of the drawings exhibited. The same spirit of helpfulness was shown by all who followed them, but the work accomplished by these two was specially great. Donald Sutcliffe, who began his interest in the collection as a schoolboy, continues it as a man, and has given me much help in the revision of these proofs.

This is, perhaps, a convenient place for me to

record other happy memories in connexion with the Ruskin collection at Bembridge. It was opened by Mr. Albert Rutherston on November 19, 1930, and we are reminded of that occasion by his gift of one of his water-colour drawings which now hangs in the collection.

In 1931 we accepted an invitation from the Arts Club of the University of Oxford to lend fifty of our pictures for a special exhibition at Oxford lasting for several weeks. That exhibition was opened by Sir Michael Sadler, and an address was given by the present writer, who recalls it now because it gave him the opportunity of shattering the legend that Ruskin was responsible either for the architect's design for the Oxford Science Museum or—a more preposterous suggestion—for the pseudo-gothic villas which adorn some of the suburbs of Oxford.

We had a special pleasure in this Oxford exhibition owing not only to the interest it created but— why should I not own up?—to the fact that we, a school founded less than twenty years ago, had received an invitation for association in this way with representatives of art in a University founded in the twelfth century.

We have presented some of Ruskin's drawings to the Italian nation, and they were placed in the Capitoline Museum in Rome. Another was presented to the Pope and is now in the Vatican Collection. Except for these there are no original works by Ruskin in the public galleries of Italy so far as is known.

Our hope was to make known to the Italian people the beauty of Ruskin's work and its influence in promoting the love of Italy on the part of English people.

The galleries at Bembridge contain pictures by some important contemporaries and friends of Ruskin, including Albert Goodwin, R.A., Sir E. Burne-Jones, Walter Crane, T. M. Rooke, Fairfax Murray, Arthur Severn, Joseph Severn, W. G. Collingwood, Edward Clifford, and others. They contain also many drawings by Old Masters including one by Tintoretto.

It has not been found possible to deal with these drawings in this volume, but I hope shortly to issue a special descriptive catalogue of them.

Finally I should like to express the interest and pleasure we have had in the visits of friends from many of the countries of the world who desired to see our collections. This has meant that we have forged permanent links of friendship, not only with individuals, but with many societies in other countries. It is good to feel that the spirit of peace is thus extended, for the man in whose honour this collection was formed was in the truest sense of the word a great peacemaker.

J. H. W.

Bembridge
September 1938

Reproductions of Ruskin's Works at Bembridge School

The number in brackets refers to
the descriptive catalogue in
the previous pages

Tomb of Ilaria di Caretto, Cathedral of Lucca (1)

The Tomb of Can Signorio della Scala, Verona (2)

Mountain Rocks and Alpine Rose (6)

Study of Roofs (20)

Ironwork at Verona (32)

Detail of the Castelbarco Tomb, Verona, 1869 (34)

Florence: Ponte Vecchio (40)

Fribourg (47)

Stuttgart (50)

Near Zirl, Tyrol, 1855 (58)

Cottage at Malham, 1876 (60)

Drawing at Venice (61)

Rouen (67)

Roslin Chapel, 1838 (69)

Copy of part of Veronese's The Cuccina Family
(Dresden) (70)

Copy of part of Botticelli's Zipporah's Flock
(Sistine Chapel, Rome) (72)

Detail from Tintoretto's Adoration of the Magi (80)

Copy of part of Tintoretto's Crucifixion (Venice) (82)

Abbeville Cathedral (87)

Grand Canal, Venice (89)

A Vineyard Walk, Lucca (114)

Map of Scotland, 1828 (120)

Roses from Dress of Central Figure of
Botticelli's Spring (125)

Lago di Sarola, 1835 (146)

Bridge at Venice (153)

Mer de Glace from the Montanvert (161)

Village, Lake, and Mountains, 1835 (155)

Mountain and Lake Scene (208)

Buildings at Verona (247)

Abbeville (248)

Bridge at Terni, 1840 (253)

Tower of the Guinigi Palace, Lucca, 1845 (255)

Hôtel de Ville, Louvain (259)

Street Scene (263)

San Miniato, Florence (268)

Château Lausanne, Sunrise, 1845 (284)

Houses at Naples, 1840 or 1841 (286)

Salerno, 1841 (288)

The Avocet (291)

From the Col de la Seigne (304)

Lucerne (307)

Three Towers (311)

Market-place in Italian Town (326)

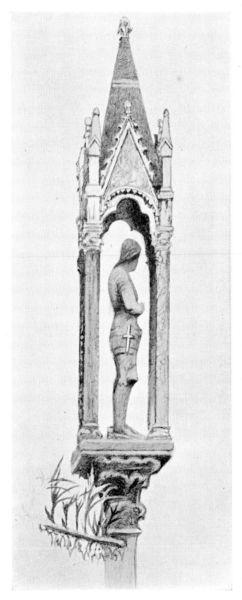

Detail from Tomb of Can Signorio
della Scala, Verona (327)

Detail from Tomb of Can Grande della Scala, Verona (330)

Tree Study at Vevey (331)

The Great St. Bernard (332)

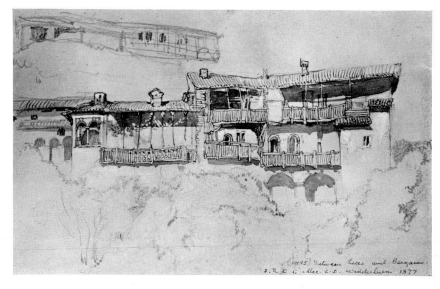

Study of Roofs and Balconies, 1845 (333)

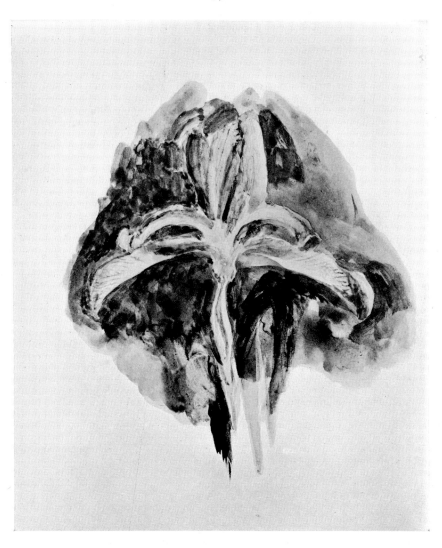

Study of an Iris (334)

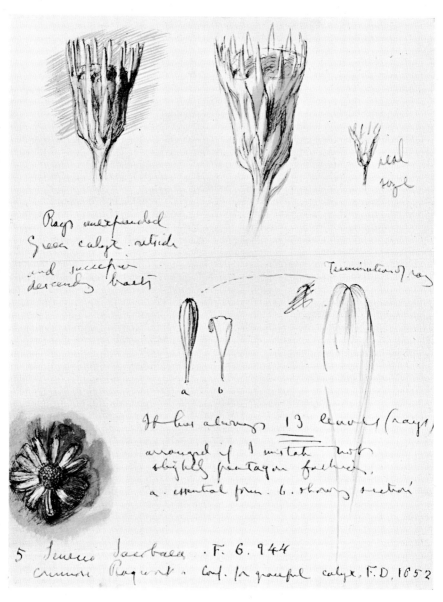

Rays unexpanded
Green calyx. outside
and successive
descending bracts

Terminates of ray

a   b

It has always 13 leaves (rays)
arranged if I mistake not
slightly pentagon fashion,
a. essential from. b. showing section

5 Senecio Jacobaea . F. 6. 944
Crimson Ragwort . Conf. for graceful calyx, F.D, 1652

Botanical Studies (335)

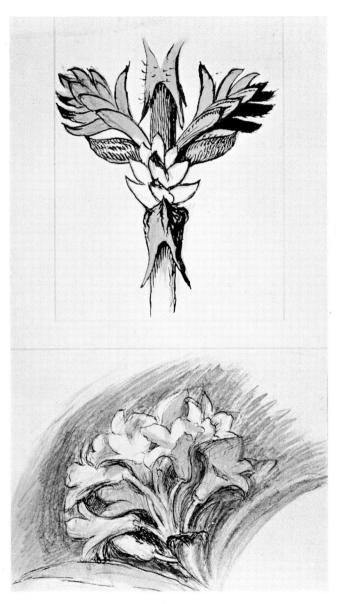

Botanical Studies (336)

Botanical Studies, 1882 (337)

Botanical Studies, 1878 (338)

Botanical Studies (339)

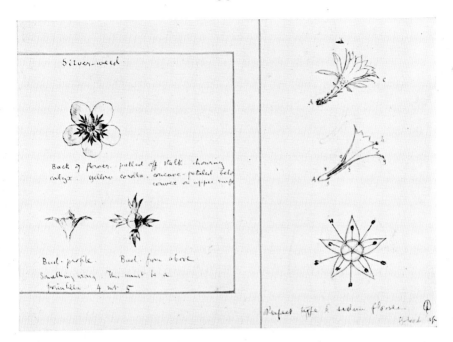

Botanical Studies (340)

Hôtel de Ville, Brussels (341)

Study of Cottages (342)

Study of a Piece of Rock with Quartz Veining (343)

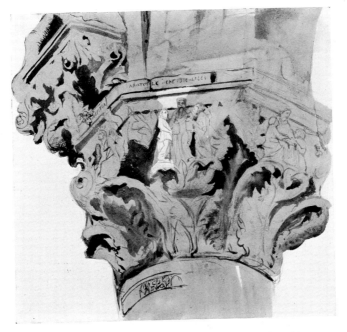

Capital, Ducal Palace, Venice (126)

Gateway of a college at
Maidstone inside view

A page from Ruskin's First Sketch-book (344)

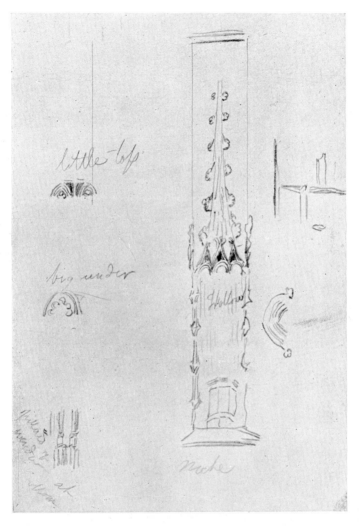

Another page from Ruskin's
First Sketch-book (345)

Bremgarten, 1860 (7)

La Résidence, Munich, 1835 (45)

Great Square, Bienne (204)

Fribourg: The Watch Tower (5)

Rheinfelden (133)

Mountain Village (101)

PRINTED IN
GREAT BRITAIN
AT THE
UNIVERSITY PRESS
OXFORD
BY
JOHN JOHNSON
PRINTER
TO THE
UNIVERSITY